"Richard has done a fantasti
and opportunities in innovati
in the crushing competitiveness of the Chinese market, along with
plenty of experience in the west, he brings a nuanced, global view
to what it takes to drive innovation. But perhaps the biggest challenge is how to take innovations out of the lab and into the real
world. Read his book and learn what it takes."

Brett King, International Bestselling Author of
Bank 4.0 and *Augmented,* Founder of Moven

"Get help to transform your Digital Strategy with this fantastic
guidebook on Innovation Labs. Learn from best practices and
failures to ensure your business will survive the digital disruption.
A must-read for anyone serious about successful innovation!"

Susanne Chishti, CEO FINTECH Circle and the
FINTECH Circle Institute, Co-Editor of
Three Bestsellers: *The FINTECH Book*,
The WEALTHTECH Book and
The INSURTECH Book

"Dive deep into Richard's narrative and resurface better aware
of your optimal approach to innovation lab excellence. He looks
beyond the hype for a practical approach to the design of innovation programs that prioritize human factors above and beyond
technological wizardry."

Paolo Sironi, IBM Fintech Thought Leader and Author of
*Fintech Innovation: From Robo-Advisors to
Goal-Based Investing and Gamification*

"Too many organizations seem to believe that if they launch an innovation lab and make some splashy announcements, meaningful progress will somehow magically occur. Turrin knows better than that. His new, comprehensive book is a must-read for all corporations that are taking their labs and innovation seriously."

Gregg M. Schoenberg, Managing Partner, Wescott Inc., Former Publisher and Co-founder of The Financial Revolutionist

"I've never known Rich to pull any punches, and the whole innovation scene needs a bloody nose to make it honest. Rich delivers a thorough going-over here that may be the reset your lab needs. If you're in the innovation business this book will help you keep it real and do it better."

Aki Ranin, Co-founder and COO, Bambu

"I used to look at insurance company innovation labs from afar and shake my head. My view then was that innovation is not something that can be bottled, bolted on, bought in, or poured over like a fancy sauce on a day-old meal. That was until I met Rich Turrin. Few have observed this scene more closely than Rich, who's been in the transformation business for most of his career. He's nurtured it, advised it and has now written the authoritative book on the subject. If anyone's got a credible view of the matter, it's Rich."

Walter de Oude, CEO, Singapore Life

INNOVATION LAB EXCELLENCE

Digital Transformation from Within

RICHARD TURRIN

INNOVATION LAB EXCELLENCE:
DIGITAL TRANSFORMATION FROM WITHIN
By Richard Turrin
1. TEC000000 2. BUS070030 3. TEC062000
Paperback ISBN: 978-1-949642-07-0
Ebook ISBN: 978-1-949642-08-7
Hardcover ISBN: 978-1-949642-09-4
Library of Congress Control Number: 2019932742

Cover design by Lewis Agrell

Printed in the United States of America

Authority Publishing
Gold River, CA
www.AuthorityPublishing.com

DEDICATION

To my beloved Sharon whose radiance permeates my life.

ACKNOWLEDGMENTS

Many have contributed to this book, a few knowingly. The majority never knew that their stories would help me see the common thread that unites them all. To all those from the lab world who told me a story that celebrated their success, or sought solace after failure, I thank you.

Several people knowingly and freely gave their time and advice to help complete this book. Gregg Schoenberg helped me see beyond the immediate success of labs to consider a day when they might be at risk of cutbacks. Mayda Lim provided insight into the Singaporean way of doing business and how labs meant so much more to the "little red dot."

Many acknowledge colleagues new and old, as do I, but few have a single colleague who is both. Paolo Sironi has been a colleague twice—during our younger years in banking and more recently at IBM. Paolo's writings inspired this book and his gift of expertise and support is reflected in these pages. Thank you, Paolo.

My editor and old friend Christa Weil-Menegas was able to help me find my voice in writing because she knows it so well in person. Her ability to summon my "pull no punches" tone, no matter how tortured the prose, helped make this project a reality. Her insistence that my writing "really wasn't that bad" helped far more than she will ever know.

Final thanks go out to my wife Sharon who supported this book throughout the journey. Her love and encouragement was the sunshine that nurtured this project to fruition.

FOREWORD

Financial institutions are facing unprecedented pressure to keep pace with innovation and transform their business models with secure and sustainable digital offerings. The upsurge of competition from global technology companies and fintech startups is forcing an inflection point: go digital or die. Unfortunately, the transition isn't easy. There is no simple route to innovation, and no fixed pathway toward digital transformation. Indeed, the recent history of digital platform implementation seems to suggest that only a handful of transformations will be successful.

Whether it's in banking or another industry, it is difficult for incumbents to approach their innovation refit as a trip back to first principles, rebuilding from there. Reinventing a company from the ground up is hobbled by practical considerations of legacy systems, existing business practices, and organizational structure. Because of this, most companies prefer a stopgap alternative, plugging in new technology incrementally and transforming in stages. Both approaches have pros and cons, which CEOs and their boards need to consider carefully. In truth, many firms seem to apply innovation simply as a cosmetic, using it to accentuate the positive while real problems remain underneath.

How then to transform innovation from wishful thinking into real change? That is the role of Innovation Labs, which face a monumental challenge. They are tasked with the extraordinary responsibility of ensuring the very survival of their institutions. They have remits on multiple fronts. These include understanding the technology that exists today and those with a promising future; knowing the competition, including entities down the road from a myriad of startup entrepreneurs; designing a roadmap for disruptive change that must overcome ingrained habits and years of obsolete "best practices"; and winning the hearts and minds of colleagues whose jobs will change or disappear.

Given these challenges, I believe that a playbook is needed to help innovation labs devise the best course of action. I truly welcome Richard Turrin's contribution to the topic, which is grounded in many years of interaction with innovation centres. Richard makes no secret of the challenges. He looks beyond the hype for a practical approach to the design of innovation programs that prioritize human factors above and beyond technological wizardry. The core of innovation is people, with our drive, our skills and also our limitations. Digital innovation represents a shift in mindset that must be sold to the organisation and embraced by all interested parties well before the technological hurdles are surmounted.

Dive deep into Richard's narrative, and resurface better aware of your optimal approach to innovation lab excellence.

Paolo Sironi
IBM Fintech Thought Leader and Author

PREFACE

My career in finance and technology has been anything but a straight line. This, above all, is the tell-tale sign of a natural innovator. The zigs and zags of moving companies and countries has honed my instinct to a razor's edge and given me insight as to how to shepherd innovation through "the system," regardless of where I happen to be and how many colleagues are telling me that "it can't be done."

Throughout my career, the one constant has been designing and building new financial products that were born from, and depended on, the latest technology. The link between product and digital technology that arguably began with the first mainframes isn't new, but the magnitude of disruption they are now causing within established businesses is on a completely new scale. The first wave of digitization that I experienced was on the trading floors in the 90's and with online retail. These disrupted limited pockets of our economy. Now rapid digitization of entire sectors is taking place in what appears to be a winner-take-all race to achieve the killer digital platform. The cost of entry is low—an internet site and an idea is all it takes—allowing everyone from start-ups to global digital giants to take aim at incumbents' most profitable business lines, if not their entire business. Incumbents are scrambling to find the right balance of innovation and digital transformation that allows them to simultaneously establish a foothold in new digital business, while not burning down their legacy operations and the critical talent within.

Innovation labs aren't new, nor is innovation. They've been called many things over the years and the concept that innovation is a critical part of any business predates the industrial age. What is different and noteworthy within the past 25 years of digital history, in my experience, is the speed with which innovation is transforming our world. We now demand "innovation on tap" and to deliver this, the process of innovation has evolved to become rigorous and studied. Waiting for innovation to occur by chance or lucky break won't do, nor will allowing it to languish at the whims of those technophobes who would kill it. If innovation labs do one thing, they give innovation a home within your company, which allows it to flourish and improve your chances of survival in the Darwinian process of digital evolution.

Innovation will always have detractors. Throughout my career I've been told that the products and technologies I was working on were frivolous, unnecessary or ill-conceived. Sometimes they were right! More often they were wrong. I remained committed to challenging the status quo throughout my career and that keeps me in better stead now than it did in my youth. If you are an innovator reading this book, I've got your back. Much of what I write is decidedly from the perspective of the innovator. That said, some of my suggestions may be counterintuitive. As a leader of innovation teams in corporate settings for many years I learned that innovation has to try to mold to the confines of corporate structure. It's not that the innovation itself is confined, so much as how we present, develop and sell its benefits to bring it to fruition.

Organization of this book

This book focuses on both how to cultivate innovation and how to foster its success within the constraints of a corporate environment. It promotes a series of best practices that may be used individually or in totality to optimize your innovation experience. It is designed to stimulate discussion and perhaps break a few taboos in the process.

As the book is aimed for business-side readers as well as those coming from the tech side, the examples are presented without jargon or deep dives into the nuts and bolts. I have, however, dedicated Chapters 22 and 23 to describing the basic technology your lab will use, and how best to work with early AI projects. Readers who are just beginning their digital journey might opt to read these chapters first if they feel the need to catch up on some basics. These chapters are designed to demystify the technologies used in labs and how best to apply them. The chapters were placed after the main discussion on innovation labs to make the flow of the content more manageable for lab people, who already know these technologies and wish to get straight to best practices.

Part I ~ The Case for Innovation Labs

Chapters 1 through 3 set the stage by examining the root reasons why labs are necessary in our current culture, and where they have come from historically. These chapters outline why you need an innovation lab, and explore the digital changes that have occurred which mandate their existence. I investigate a few alternatives, but in the end a laboratory is a practical way to concentrate the skills you need to complete a transformation in-house. I also look at the historical context of labs, particularly a recent example in which codified rules replicate many of the rules we use in Agile development, but in fact predates Agile by 50 years. This historical observation helps contextualize the use of innovation labs today. We live in unique and interesting times that require special application of technology, but our grandparents' generation understood the concept of nurturing innovation that still offers lessons to this day.

Part II ~ Best Practices

Chapter 4 introduces the central theme of the book: a series of twelve best practices which, if implemented in whole or part, will increase the efficiency and quality of innovation at your laboratory. The best practices are examined case by case in subsequent chapters. I do not expect readers to immediately recognize themselves or their laboratories from a quick read of the best practices in Chapter 4. No laboratory will have all of these issues, but certainly every laboratory will have some. If some of them resonate, the reader can go directly to the chapter of interest to learn the practical applications for the laboratory.

Optimally, readers should scan all the chapters in the order they are presented. The examples and problem-solving may apply to issues you were unaware of, but are now able to discern. What's more, the best practices are cumulative and a reader might miss out on benefits if chapters are skipped. They appear roughly in order of overall importance. In each I use real examples, which should help the reader recognize familiar situations and roadblocks: "that's just like our lab," setting the stage for fixing them.

Chapters 5 through 16 lay out the best practices in detail. Each has examples of what happens when the practices are ignored, and others where they have been applied with success. Each chapter also provides actions to take to help get your lab more closely aligned with best practices. The starting point for all change is issue-spotting, followed by collaborative steps to resolve problems.

For this reason, the best practices in Chapters 5 through 16 are calibrated to begin discussion among the lab, management, and business units that use the lab. I fully expect that if representatives from these three factions read the same chapter one may say "that's us" and the others may say "we already do that." Discovering that a misunderstanding exists means the parties are ready to get productive. Clarity is necessary on roles and shared responsibilities. All too often with innovation labs these hard discussions don't happen because they are simply too painful or end up accusatory. With a guide in hand with real examples from other labs, such discussions are easier to initiate and more focused on finding a solution. If a discussion ensues, I've been successful, and if concrete actions are taken that eventually get all three in agreement, I'd love to hear from you.

Part III ~ Why Do Labs Fail?

Chapters 17 through 20 deal with common patterns of failure in laboratories. It's no secret that some labs are underperforming. Having seen more than my fair share up close I came to recognize that there are typical clusters of disregard, almost like a doctor recognizes the flu by a combination of fever, cough, and runny nose. Each symptom helps to confirm the diagnosis. In these chapters I discuss what the most common patterns are and the strong medicine required to correct the problem.

If you read Chapters 17-20 and see similarities in your lab, you have some deeply rooted problems to deal with. You will have to retrofit a number of the best practices outlined in Chapters 5-16, and likely deal with a major cultural transformation from within your lab, its parent or both. All is not lost! Even an ailing lab can be coaxed back to health if all the parties recognize the symptoms and patterns of illness.

Part IV ~ Elements of Successful Labs

Chapter 21 is a brief introduction on how to measure performance. While no two labs have the same goals and objectives, there needs to be a flexible system in place to determine if the lab is performing. For many labs this is an afterthought, because there is no agreed standard for success. In most cases labs won't have a huge success that defines their overall value. In fact, the most successful labs have many small wins that can easily fly under the radar.

The closing Chapters 24 and 25 speak to the longevity of innovation labs. There are two fundamental questions that need to be examined. The first is, are labs the first on the chopping block when a down market hits, or are they a potential savior? The second is, are innovations simply the latest passing management fad? I invite the reader to press on to these chapters for the answers that demonstrate that innovation labs are not only a trend, but are the foundation for change that will ensure a company's survival well into the future.

CONTENTS

PART I

The Case for Innovation Labs

THE INNOVATION LAB

Innovation is upon us. It seems that nearly every day a new laboratory, space, studio, or center opens, complete with espresso machines, open plan seating and exotic murals. Fill it with twentysomethings dressed in jeans and t-shirts who are all pictures of digital mastery, bake for about six months, and innovation will flow like a fountain.

If only it were so easy.

In fact, most of the labs I've had the pleasure of visiting are underperforming, despite the investment in espresso machines and modern architecture. It's not that they are going to go bust (thanks to their parent's deep pockets), but the innovations emerging from these facilities fail to meet the expectations of senior management, or the young innovators are dispirited and feel they are capable of more. In many cases no one is truly happy and the labs themselves are taking a hit.

What emerges from my experience consulting for these facilities and talking with employees and managers is a consistent picture. The main problem is how these innovation labs are—or more accurately, aren't—integrated into their parent. Addressing these integration problems effectively will enable the true potential of innovation at your company. This is what will separate the winners from losers in innovation wars.

Every company needs innovation; the question of course is: How do you get there? Until recently most industrial sectors did not have a codified plan for innovation at their organisations. There were three exceptions, the first being consumer-products labs, actual laboratories to test new product ideas, where they devised new flavors or other selling points. The second sector was the dedicated and highly-funded research division, typically in technology companies, where long-term and possibly blue-sky research was carried out and patiently shepherded into products that might be launched into the market ten years later. While these research labs are innovative and responsible for countless breakthroughs, they are distinct from today's digital innovation labs. Both the time scale and the objectives are different. The third exception— "skunkworks"—is comprehensively discussed in a later chapter. It arose from manufacturing during the exigencies of war and the need to speed the adoption of new technologies.

> *57% of respondents said their companies do not follow formal innovation processes.*
>
> CB Insights, "State of Innovation" Survey of 677 Corporate Strategy Executives

There are two more "non-plans" for developing innovation that are in use by many companies. The first is to simply wait patiently to copy the innovation of others. While it does not guarantee industry preeminence, it does ensure that all things being equal the company does not fall too far behind. Large, well-established companies may use this strategy to keep ahead of a scrappier and more innovative competitor. In the digital era however, upstarts can topple incumbents with surprising speed. Second, there is the lone wolf manager (who comes along very rarely) who really likes innovation and creates something new and surprises everyone with its success. While these self-directed initiatives are welcome, they are certainly not innovation that you can count on or plan for.

Enter our new digital world. Regardless of what business sector you're in, the concept of innovation and the subsequent production pipeline has changed. The old-school, tried-and-true approach to bringing new products to consumers—whether they were new soft drinks or new investment products—no longer works because digital innovation has fundamentally altered baseline expectations of speed to market. Advances in digital technology have changed how we reach our clients, what they expect from us, and the methodology we use to innovate. The new digital world has rendered our traditional innovation approaches incompatible with our new ultra-fast-to-market digital world.

Basic research is somewhat removed from this cycle—it usually can't be rushed, and there will always be a need for long-term investigation to create something new and lasting. But there's a new intermediary, one that sits between basic research and the demand for lightning response. This is the innovation lab, which seeks to create a digital advantage for your company via innovation across its activities.

The wold's largest taxi company owns no taxis: **Uber**	The worlds largest movie company owns no theaters: **Netflix**
The world's largest accommodation provider owns no property: **Airbnb**	The world's largest money market fund has no brokers: **Yu'ebao**
Some of the largest software vendors don't write their code: **Apple and Google Apps**	The world's largest media owners create no content: **Facebook, Youtube, Wechat**

Digital disruption is upon us and has turned traditional business models on their head.

Digital disruption throws a proverbial spanner/wrench in the works of many traditional industry sectors that have yet to adopt it because it changes the product delivery mechanism, fundamentally alters the business model, or exposes the company to more nimble competition. Digital is a new world to many senior executives in these companies. How best to harness a paradigm-changing technology is very much a mystery to most. This is particularly true of executives who spent a lifetime honing skills on business-building, only to see it thrashed by digital competitors. As a result, many sectors, financial services being one of them, are now plunging headlong into digitization. Like it or not, executives are going digital as fast as possible, while *simultaneously* trying to solve the problem of how best to introduce digital into their business. Their superficially rational solution is to bring as many digitally enabled people on board as possible, and get them to work.

Eureka, we have the digital innovation laboratory, populated by a group purposefully assembled to transform a given business through their digital expertise. The lab is bolted on to the existing non-digital company just like training wheels on a child's bicycle. Like them, the lab is to be used for a fixed period, then taken off once the company learns how to manage digital innovation on its own. Or at least that's the theory. No one can provide a confident estimate of how long it takes to graft digital sophistication into a company. It's never been done—so anyone suggesting that this will take two years or ten is just guessing.

Conceiving these labs as a discrete unit makes sense since it's impossible to hire enough digital people to put them everywhere in the company. A centralized resource is what's practical. This also serves a second motive: A company can show off its lab to shareholders, analysts or rating agencies, to demonstrate how innovative the company is and how this will translate into future earnings. It ticks off the innovation box, neatly, cleanly, and with certainty. One tour of an innovation lab with its dancing robots will dispel any concern that the main business—products and delivery channels—are obsolete.

At this point it's important to clarify that the concept of a dedicated innovation lab has undeniable benefits. For one, it is practical. Digital expertise is so expensive, and in such short supply, it is impossible to pay for and disperse these people within the company. In addition, diluting digital competence in this way is counterproductive, because there are invariably solutions that require a team pulling together in hard work. Concentrating tech skills under one roof solves multiple problems. By focusing resources a company can, in theory, create a center of excellence that serves the entire institution and moreover enforces continuity in digital adoption and innovation throughout the organization. In addition this concentrates the "disruptive" elements in a single spot, making it easier to monitor the outcome. At least this is the theory – the pitfalls lie in how this is practiced.

Digital labs created more recently outside of the tech sector are relatively young; the oldest has been active for less than a decade. Evidence of their success is both highly variable and shrouded in corporate secrecy. It's often public knowledge, for example, when an innovation lab throws a hackathon, but we don't know whether the AI-backed product recently introduced by your competitor came from their lab, or elsewhere. There is no doubt that some labs have launched significant products and services. Others seem to languish in the background, never quite attaining the promised extent of digital transformation within the parent.

Innovation labs are like rock-n-roll bands. With many of the early labs, management seemed undecided on whether they wanted a monster number-one hit, or a string of songs that hang lower on the charts year after year. As time and experience running labs accrues, it's becoming clear that labs are best part of a longer-term strategy, meaning that staying power on the pop charts is critical. It's increasingly evident that the metrics of laboratory success are less likely tied to the number of hackathons sponsored per year (the innovation equivalent of a number-one hit), but instead the *depth of digital adoption* by the parent company. This is changing our perceptions of the labs' ultimate role, and more significantly, how we run them to fulfill this role.

This matters because the labs that were initiated early on may need to undergo significant changes in policy and operations as management better understands how to maximize benefits. It's important to point out that no one has done anything wrong here. New solutions require time and experience to settle into best practice. And it seems clear that while there are multiple measures of lab effectiveness, fostering digital adoption that reaches deep into the corporate parent is paramount. Why? Because it creates a profound long-term effect on the psyche of fellow employees that in aggregate is preferable, and healthier to a company's prospects, than a one-hit wonder.

In the middle of all of this innovation arms race are the people who deal with the lab on a daily basis. I wrote this book for them. My goal was to create a guide to help them understand the conditions in which innovation will flourish. Who will benefit most from this book? The lab manager and employees are first on the list. They understand their lab's challenges better than anyone else but need a guide that can act as an independent point of reference. Something that they can point to, or reference a chapter from, that will help them explain that they are not alone when they voice a concern or tackle a problem. At various points in my career when I was in the thick of an innovation quandary, I would have liked to have had it on my desk with a few post-its and yellow highlights to show others how to think their way out of trouble spots. It certainly would have helped. It's no secret that many lab managers are in the earlier stages of their career and may not have the seasoning that their corporate colleagues do. This book will give perspective on how to work with others in their company and moreover explain why brilliant efforts are often met with nothing more than a strained smile. It's not you; it's due to the real anxiety that comes when innovation threatens entrenched interests.

This book is also of great benefit to senior executives overseeing the lab. This might include the CEO who funds it, the Chief Innovation Officer (CINO) who oversees it, or the CIO that fumes about the lab wrecking his systems. All need to understand the practical realities of the innovation business, as it is most likely a new experience. Simply put, managing an innovation team is different. The objectives for this team are special and need attention. Think of your new lab as a seedling needing constant attention to environmental conditions or it simply won't grow. Your existing businesses run by seasoned veterans thrive on benign neglect. This book will be gold in their hands as it will help them recognize and head off the problems that they'll run into before they compromise the lab's mission or efficiency. It will give them insights to help them make their expensive new lab more effective and produce the innovation they desperately desire more quickly.

Finally, and with probably the greatest amount of empathy, this book was written for the business unit leaders who may never have heard of an innovation lab before and are now being asked to work with one. They are the ones being asked to make the biggest cultural leap. They have to take products or services that they have invested a lifetime in perfecting and use technology to disrupt them. In many cases this will be relatively painless and yield results that show big wins for everyone. In other cases it won't be so clear or end in smiles. The review of a process or procedure showing that a life's work can now be automated may be humbling to the core. Even with the best of project outcomes, a manager can expect the innovation process to be uncomfortable. Every preconceived notion of how you conduct business will be examined and you can fully expect that someone much younger than you will inevitably say something along the lines of "oh that's stupid." For you this book will be indispensable. The rules are changing around you and this book will help you understand how the game of innovation is played. It will give you power to help you work effectively with the innovation team and get the best results possible out of your efforts. Just as the lab manager can benefit from an independent point of reference, so can you. This book will help you understand how innovation is done and can give you a reference point to guide your team. It can help avoid misunderstandings and hopefully get you more innovation with less work.

WHY YOU NEED ONE

I 'll give it to you straight: Innovation labs are necessary to promote digital adoption in your company. Yes, I criticize them now and again, but that is solely intended to temper—to moderate—the attitude toward them. I am not a proponent of the over-hyped claims of digital nirvana that some consultants shill with a lab's start-up. But I am even more skeptical of companies that cower from the digital challenges that lie in wait and as a consequence do nothing.

Let there be no confusion. Innovation labs present an opportunity to promote digital within your organization and are fundamentally a positive if run correctly. My caveat lies in how we run these labs. This is critical to getting anything of value out of them. Too many companies have made tremendous investments and received very little demonstrable payout. These enclaves are not a panacea or cure-all for your digital ailments. It is best to temper your expectations at the outset. The lab itself is merely a *component* of your digital program, albeit an important one. Without cultural and managerial changes pressed from all directions, the lab is doomed to fail.

It may be helpful to take one big step back, and address how a company might address digital disruption *without* instituting a dedicated lab. The facile approach would be to task one or several business-unit leaders to adopt digital processes within their business lines and simply rely on the IT department to make it all happen. The results will be obvious in about a year. It's reliant on pre-existing resources, and indeed may work to modernize a product line, or refresh a service. Good over the short term, but there's a problem with this strategy. It's a patch: It doesn't acknowledge the sweeping changes that digital adoption will force—yes, force—upon your company. This really isn't about a single product line or digital fix.

Instead, the oncoming climate will upend, and demand a renegotiation of, your entire company's use of technology. Sound big? It is. That's why assigning a few trusted lieutenants to work their magic isn't a digital strategy.

This is one flaw in trying to implement change from within. But there's a bigger one, which is much more pernicious: the assumption that your staff *want* to make the transition to digital. In many cases, if not most, your existing business managers are innately reluctant. Unless they are particularly digitally minded, this is being pushed upon them and represents a major distraction from their "normal" job. People who started their career more than ten years ago did not have technical innovation in their sightlines. They wanted to be a great salesman, accountant, manager or other professional. Digital anything was not part of the big plan. Again, unless they are truly exceptional forward-thinkers, at a fundamental level digital represents an inconvenience. For this reason their ability to make transformative changes to their business will be limited. Even worse, your organization may harbor managers who willingly try to delay, postpone or even torpedo efforts aimed at digitizing their work or departments.

Let's not be shocked at this behavior. They are, after all, only human. These managers have spent a significant portion of their lives building the very structures that digital seeks to tear down. I witnessed this first hand at IBM as cloud-based services were launched, services that fundamentally changed the role of their iconic sales force. With the advent of cloud services, the IBM sales force, those of the sober ties and "any color of shirt as long as it is white," were relegated to telling customers to go on-line and purchase software from the IBM website, rather than closing the sale themselves. If ever there was a fabulous example of disruption, this would be it, since cloud services made the salesman redundant. Clients could sample the software under a free trial, see if it met their needs, and then purchase the software based on actual usage rather than the number of seats. It was a revolution in how software is sold. So which of your management team will make the recommendation to go digital, and thereby force the retirement of the sales force he or she has spent years fine tuning? It's too tough a call for most mortals and the need for third party intervention is obvious.

So if home-grown innovation is typically subject to internal biases, the alternative step would be hiring a third-party management consultant, who would present a roadmap to help you sort this out. Of course your preferred Big Four consultant would be delighted to produce a report on how digital transformation will eventually lead you to an El Dorado of profitability. Except there's a problem. As with my example of IBM, most senior partners at the Big Four or other non-digital-specific consultancies *have also been disrupted*. Most are experiencing substantial challenges in retraining themselves and, critically, attracting a younger generation of digital specialists able to blaze the optimal trail through these woods. There are clear exceptions, but digital talent within the larger consultancies is spread very thin.

In the best of circumstances, even if a consultancy provides a decent road map, they can't help you get there. Most practices have limited system-integration skills, and only recently have some actually built teams capable of effecting tech solutions. This further limits their advice because while it's correct for consultants to say "use big data," very few can recommend a specific technology that will work given your unique circumstances.

If you are unable to rely on your current management pool or your trusted consultants, you may note that your options for acquiring innovation expertise are rapidly dwindling. A third way is to go back to your IT department and charge them with bringing innovation to your company. After all, they've been the trusted gatekeepers to your systems for years, and computers lie at the heart of the challenge. But there are several problems here as well. One, already touched upon, is that the relation between tech and innovation relies on the insights and experience of the BU managers. Your IT is certainly capable of buying a system and implementing it, but they don't have the overview on how it will be used in the context of your greater digital business strategy. Hence the wave of new "Chief Innovation Officer" or CINO positions created at many large companies. In the new digital model, business unit leaders are directed to work in conjunction with tech providers to understand how best to use technology to reach their clients. This is something that your IT department—as skilled as it may be—would struggle mightily to achieve on its own.

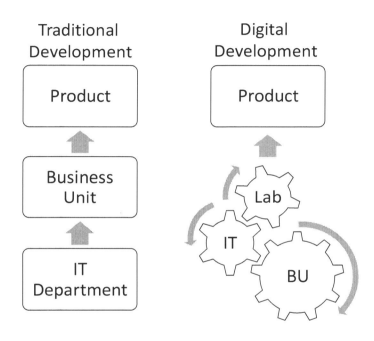

The digital model has disrupted the traditional role of the IT department with new digital products made in collaborative efforts.

But there's a second issue with tasking IT that arguably reaches even deeper. As the gatekeepers of tech and the arbiters of tech orthodoxy at your company, the typical IT department isn't structured to implement the newest digital technologies on offer. In the past their job may have been to buy and implement new software, a fairly straightforward role (though one that can be fraught, as we've all experienced at some point). In our new, second-wave stage of digital adoption, they are being asked to analyze the customer-centricity of a sales process or train a newly-purchased AI. These entail new mindsets and skill sets, which are frankly disruptive to them as well. Digital transformation has been a major shock for IT departments—and not necessarily a positive one. Entire IT teams are being stripped out and replaced as system after system goes on to cloud computing platforms (like those provided by Amazon Web Service), and as the methods by which we build and implement technology fundamentally changes. In most cases, using your existing staff in their current roles is not a compelling strategy for digital adoption. It's not that they don't want to help you, it's just that they are not capable of doing this on their own, without backup expertise in tech areas currently outside their purview.

By now you should be coming to the inescapable conclusion that tech innovation should be done in-house, with a special team. No matter what they are called, or to whom they report, some sort of innovation lab or team is the way forward. Welcome to the innovation lab business! You're not alone with your questions. Everyone has them, and everyone is learning from the examples of organisations that are forging ahead. In its report "The Spread of Innovation around the World" Capgemini Consulting reports that between March-October 2016, 88 new innovation labs opened on a global basis. In digitally advanced Singapore alone, more than 15 labs opened from Q2 2017- Q2 2018.

The innovation lab business is booming and it's not because senior managers are enamored with digital or innovation. On the contrary, this is a matter of business survival—they want to grasp how best to bring the promise of digital into their company, and to fend off any tactical superiority on the part of the competition. Whether that sounds Machiavellian or simply matter-of-fact, it's the truth. Many senior managers cutting the ribbon on their new innovation facility have no other cards to play, and innovation labs represent a reasonable, if not yet well-worn, path to attaining a desired result.

LEARNING FROM THE PAST

Innovation isn't new. Companies have been pursuing different innovation models for decades. Obviously, digital innovation provides a unique set of challenges, but the basics of innovation go back many years. It's worth looking at one specific historical example to highlight the similarities with setting up a successful program today.

Arguably one of the most famous and successful innovation teams was the "Skunk Works" at Lockheed Martin. This group, which designed state-of-the-art airplanes like the SR-71 and the U-2, got its start with the need for utter technological dominance ushered in by the Second World War. The group is so legendary that "skunkworks" entered the vernacular, meaning any innovation space or a group that was both set apart from the rest of the company and given a high degree of autonomy to work on advanced or otherwise out-of-the-box projects.

In essence, the digital labs of today are equivalent to yesterday's skunkworks. Their products may be different, but the goal of original and rapidly implemented product development is very much the same. The Skunk Works at Lockheed predates our digital world but represents an environment and behaviors we should seek to emulate.

Skunk Works leader Clarence "Kelly" Johnson was convinced that "people challenged to perform at their best will do so." He set up a system within monolithic Lockheed Martin to allow his team to innovate faster, better and cheaper than was possible within the normal constraints of the parent organization. His goal was to increase the rate of innovation at the onset of World War II and during the Cold War to produce novel kinds of airplanes. His goals are wholly in keeping with ours, especially given that we too want to do more with fewer resources, and do so rapidly enough to avoid digital obsolescence.

Fortunately for us, Kelly left us his "14 Rules and Practice" — commandments he felt were key to accomplishing lean innovation.

Kelly's 14 Rules and Practices

1. The Skunk Works manager must be delegated practically complete control of his program in all aspects. He should report to a division president or higher.
2. Strong but small project offices must be provided both by the military and industry.
3. The number of people having any connection with the project must be restricted in an almost vicious manner. Use a small number of good people (10% to 25% compared to the so-called normal systems).
4. A very simple drawing and drawing release system with great flexibility for making changes must be provided.
5. There must be a minimum number of reports required, but important work must be recorded thoroughly.
6. There must be a monthly cost review covering not only what has been spent and committed but also projected costs to the conclusion of the program.
7. The contractor must be delegated and must assume more than normal responsibility to get good vendor bids for subcontract on the project. Commercial bid procedures are very often better than military ones.
8. The inspection system as currently used by the Skunk Works, which has been approved by both the Air Force and Navy, meets the intent of existing military requirements and should be used on new projects. Push more basic inspection responsibility back to subcontractors and vendors. Don't duplicate so much inspection.
9. The contractor must be delegated the authority to test his final product in flight. He can and must test it in the initial

stages. If he doesn't, he rapidly loses his competency to design other vehicles.

10. The specifications applying to the hardware must be agreed to well in advance of contracting. The Skunk Works practice of having a specification section stating clearly which important military specification items will not knowingly be complied with and reasons therefore is highly recommended.

11. Funding a program must be timely so that the contractor doesn't have to keep running to the bank to support government projects.

12. There must be mutual trust between the military project organization and the contractor, the very close cooperation and liaison on a day-to-day basis. This cuts down misunderstanding and correspondence to an absolute minimum.

13. Access by outsiders to the project and its personnel must be strictly controlled by appropriate security measures.

14. Because only a few people will be used in engineering and most other areas, ways must be provided to reward good performance by pay not based on the number of personnel supervised.

Let's start to unpack Kelly's list in a basic way (we'll go into detail in subsequent chapters). The first thing to note when reading these rules is how they are centered around the conduct of people within the organization. How many times does he reference "technology" or "innovation?" Never. His rules are all about breaking down the behavior of people to manage the development of new technology, not about the technology itself. He is trying to promote and define the conditions and culture by which innovation can flourish in his own unique and specific environment. Building airplanes for the US government isn't exactly the same as building digital products—but the concept that you need to report to senior management (rule 1) and tackle projects with small but powerful teams (rules 2 and 3) are just as essential to digital innovators today as they were for his airplane design teams.

There is another important takeaway from Kelly's focus on people and organizational structure. Innovation isn't about the tech, but instead the people and systems used to develop and apply it. This message is just as valid today as in Kelly Johnson's time.

Don't forget it the next time you read an article that says some new technology is going to change everything. Will the tech change everything, or will the people implementing the tech be the driver of change? Kelly Johnson already gave us the answer. People—and systems that allow people to achieve their best work—are paramount in the successful implementation of technology. Why? Because tech evolves so very quickly. Your innovation lab shouldn't be a bet on blockchain, AI or any other purported wizardry. Instead, it should be a bet on individuals who are nimble enough to adapt and implement the resources that best get the job done.

Kelly's rules are helpful, but there are still a few pieces missing when we look at applying them to our innovation labs. For example, note that in rule 3 Kelly talks about using "good people" and "restricting access" to the project. While no one will argue with the former, for Kelly restricting access was a more straightforward matter. He already knew how to build an airplane. If he needed special landing gear, he could simply find the experts on landing gear at Lockheed Martin and bring them into Skunk Works.

It's not quite so easy with our teams. Of course if money is no object, we can buy the best possible blockchain or AI talent from the market. Still, that leaves us dealing with younger people with no deep appreciation of exactly how this tech will be used. Rather than Kelly's "restricted access" we need to open our doors to consultants or systems integrators—people who can help us complete our digital projects as efficiently as possible.

Returning to the rules that do well with the passage of time, 4, 5 and 12 are key. Here Kelly slashes at red tape and internal processes that slowed his work flow. So effective are these tenets that we've since codified lean, unobstructed workflows when building software through the use of "agile development." In rule 4, we actually can see how agile development's iterative nature maps nicely to the release system Kelly instituted for blueprints. Both blueprints and software are, in essence, documents that undergo rapid iterative development and must robustly withstand editing and adaptation. Likewise, in rule 5, keeping reports to a minimum has a direct corollary in code documentation, which is kept ultra-lean in agile projects. Finally, rule 12 promotes daily personal meetings, just as required in agile development through co-location and face-to-face daily briefings. In spite of the passage of time and the fact that we build different products, today's agile development shares system DNA with Kelly's rules and objectives.

Skunk Works was segregated from its corporate parent, having its own culture and a high degree of control over its budget for product development. It was in essence a start-up within the confines of a corporate parent—very much like the tech start-ups of today, with their idiosyncratic culture and mandate to bring digital innovation to life.

That is precisely what companies are striving to create with their innovation labs. They want a start-up's sense of purpose and single-minded determination to help jump-start innovation. The rules that Kelly Johnson promoted more than 60 years ago go a long way to defining the behaviors we expect from innovation teams today.

If you enjoy this book, it's a "best practice" to leave a review on Amazon. I appreciate your support in helping me get the word out to others involved with innovation. Even short reviews help more than you know.

PART II

Best Practices

I would love to meet you! Join me in "innovating our future" by sending a note on richturrin.com. Also, join in the discussion by connecting on LinkedIn: linkedin.com/in/turrin.

BEST PRACTICES FOR INNOVATING OUR FUTURE

I've had the privilege of running an innovation lab that was uniquely positioned to do two things: sell technology to other labs, and act as a "developer for hire" to create fintech for financial service clients. This meant innovation labs were both my clients and my colleagues. This gave me a unique point of view that has allowed me to analyze first-hand their failures and successes. Running IBM's innovation efforts in fintech within their "cognitive studio" (to simplify, from here onward I will designate innovation studios, labs, centers, and spaces collectively as "labs"), I've seen which corporate practices work and which clearly do not. No single lab is a perfect model for success (or failure). Rather, the aggregate of dozens of conversations with both disgruntled and happy innovators is the foundation of my observations going forward.

Singapore is a hotbed of fintech innovation. A spirit of innovation permeates the business environment, because the need to innovate is an existential dictate. Singapore has no natural resources and its location as a trading hub between East and West fuels its economy through banking and trade. Business with China provides a full 26% of Singapore's total GDP; China is as much a formidable competitor as it is an ally. To remain a banking and business leader in the region, Singapore is desperate to stay in the technological forefront. It is therefore promoting digital innovation of all forms as a means to maintain and expand its presence.

Singapore coerced the formation of innovation labs in its local companies with substantial government subsidies. As a result, it boasts global recognition as a center for fintech development. Labs of all types have flourished, each having unique characteristics.

Singapore is an incubator that offers a unique opportunity to study different labs' methodologies and interaction. The sheer number of labs, competition for talent, and government oversight—driven by the sense that getting this right is a matter of sovereign survival—create an environment every bit as fertile as Silicon Valley.

Out of this environment and my interactions with colleagues in the lab business I started to consider, like Kelly Johnson before me, what series or group of practices could be used to foster innovation in our companies. This stemmed from an analysis of which conditions led to success, and which led to failure. From this I devised a list of best practices—essentially rules of conduct—that facilitate the adoption of innovation. Instead of taking an approach that is prescriptive in a cookie-cutter way (do this, do that), these practices help foster innovation in an ever-changing and inherently unpredictable set of circumstances. Which ones we adopt or reject specifically isn't as important as recognizing that these practices in sum and in part help foster a holistic, company-wide innovation mindset.

The list of best practices that follows is a summary of more detailed analysis that I'll provide point by point in subsequent chapters. The list represents remedies for a host of symptoms that may plague labs—even those run by the best-intentioned management and staff. So let's take an overview first, and then drill down into how each of these specific practices can help turn around symptoms that you may recognize as all too familiar in your organization.

The practices I promote for innovation labs are as follows:

Turrin's Innovation Lab Best Practices

1. **Be highly visible:** The innovation lab must be highly visible to the business units it supports. The free flow of ideas among these groups is critical to bringing digital innovation to the company.
2. **Calculate return on investment (ROI):** Innovation labs should demonstrate an understanding of the ROI of the projects they propose in hard dollars, with soft dollars

only if absolutely necessary. The discipline of calculating return gives the lab common ground with management, and increases credibility.

3. **Focus on people not tech:** The focus of the lab must be on promoting people's relationship to technology rather than promoting the technology itself. Implementing technology is most successful when it has the backing of the people who use it. Technology by itself won't transform your company; people using it will.

4. **Say no to carte blanche:** Labs need freedom to innovate, but moderate boundaries help them perform better because all parties have clearer expectations on outcomes. Labs should never have carte blanche to freely innovate.

5. **Balance staffing:** Finding balance between staff with domain experience and digital innovators who by nature lack this experience is critical and a constant challenge. Most labs tilt toward having a majority of new digital employees who must be trained to understand your business.

6. **Avoid the "big plan":** Labs should recalibrate their desire for a "big plan" with large ambitions to smaller, more achievable projects that show consistent progress.

7. **Buy don't build:** In most cases, labs should not be building their own technology but instead be buying tech from the open market. This reduces time to market, lowers costs, and ensures that the best solutions are implemented.

8. **Use disciplined project management:** Acknowledge that project management with innovation is difficult. It requires flexibility and toughness in equal measure. Many project goals are challenging to attain. Killing off projects that have failed or stalled is humane and conserves tight resources.

9. **Flip your hackathon:** Hackathons for staff greatly promote internal innovation. Hackathons for students are yesterday's solution and do little to either bring innovation to your lab or reach promising students.

10. **Transform, not disrupt:** Your lab's goal should be transformation, not disruption. This helps to help foster an environment of inclusion among your staff and avoids the fear and confrontation that can occur when lab staff attempt to undercut process or procedures.

11. **The CINO vs the CIO:** A Chief Innovation Officer is necessary as a focal point for promoting innovation to senior management. It may seem expedient to hand innovation to your CIO or CTO, but both may view innovation as a secondary objective.

12. **Avoid inflated expectations:** Inflated expectations for labs are common, and merely building a lab is not sufficient to bring innovation to your company. The interplay among your lab, business units, and internal control functions like IT and compliance needs to be examined for success.

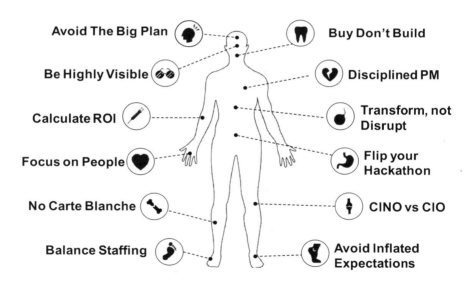

Avoid The Big Plan
Be Highly Visible
Calculate ROI
Focus on People
No Carte Blanche
Balance Staffing

Buy Don't Build
Disciplined PM
Transform, not Disrupt
Flip your Hackathon
CINO vs CIO
Avoid Inflated Expectations

Turrin's Innovation Lab Best Practices as a path to good health. Which ones we adopt or reject specifically isn't as important as recognizing that these practices in sum and in part help foster a holistic, company-wide innovation mindset.

Each of the 12 conditions I've outlined comes from direct observation of labs that were successes or failures. Note that I've visited far more labs that struck me as failing than those that appeared successful. A factor here may be that given a sympathetic ear, lab personnel will gripe that no one understands what they want to do, but overriding this is the fact that labs are still in the experimental stages. The rules for management haven't been standardized and all companies are feeling their way through this new resource as best they can. No one starts a lab with the intent of failure, but through benign neglect or displaced good intentions many labs simply aren't living up to expectations.

If you manage or are responsible for an innovation lab, the chapters that follow, which provide a detailed analysis of each of the 12 best practices in turn, should prove enlightening. They specify what can go wrong when the practice isn't followed, how to recognize symptoms of neglect or mismanagement, and how to address the situation in each case. It's unlikely you'll have all of these shortcomings at once in your lab; instead, read through and see which sound just a bit like what you're experiencing. If there's a similarity, it's a good bet that you've got a problem and need to take steps to fix it.

I've made some suggestions for how to fix common lab problems, but please bear in mind that every lab and situation is unique. There is no guarantee that the solutions I propose will work verbatim. Think of them instead as a starting point for discussion, to open a dialogue on the baseline conditions that will help make your lab more productive.

Lab staff reading this book should enjoy the best practices that follow. This is a "greatest hits" of problems at innovation labs, taken from real life. I'm sure you'll see yourself in more than one chapter. Maybe you can use a few of the solutions to make your lab work better from the inside, or maybe they'll be a good starting point for external discussions with management. Either way, by having a reference point you can at least start the process of changing your work environment for the better without making it all up as you go along. As an innovator you are no doubt aware of the need to show examples or references on how something worked elsewhere to pique interest in a new solution. If some of the stories in this book serve this role than I've done the entire innovation community a service.

Take note that if your lab isn't working to its full potential there is a shared responsibility for fixing it, and I don't lay blame at the feet of the laboratory in every case. I try to be as objective as possible when assigning responsibility for the problems I've seen, even though my background working within labs makes me slightly biased. While some of my best practices may cast blame on the labs themselves, others point to poor management practices by the lab's parent at formation. Regardless of where the problem originates, the need to work collectively to resolution is in everyone's best interest.

BE HIGHLY VISIBLE

The single largest issue causing innovation labs to fail is that they are invisible to the business units they seek to transform. The two sides don't meet around the coffee machine, don't attend common staff meetings, and are often housed far apart. Is it any wonder that they don't produce stunning innovation?

Secluding an innovation team (usually with the aim of intensifying their focus) has a counterproductive effect: They become so isolated that they barely understand the demanding business needs of the companies they serve. They are apart, alone, and frankly out of touch. I never cease to be amazed, when talking to employees at a bank, how few know the name of the innovation lab head or what they are up to. Nothing speaks louder to me of a failing innovation program than the deafening silence of being unknown and unused by the business side. This may paint a picture of fault resting with these executives. But it's a two-way street. The outreach can be equally poor by those in charge of the innovation lab.

As a case in point, I recently worked on a consulting engagement for a large bank. My role was to promote innovation to their staff. As part of my background research I reached out to the innovation lab and asked for examples of business unit leaders who were active in working with the innovation team. The lab had been in operation for more than three years and was the obvious cornerstone of the bank's innovation operations. They were active as an accelerator, held hackathons and got fairly regular press coverage for their technical wizardry. I chatted with the lab head surrounded by an open plan office staffed with young people who just radiated innovation. I asked for the names of people from the business units to interview, to get their perspective on innovation. What came next shocked me. I got the names of only three people from the business units, who were involved in a grand total of two projects from the lab. One of the projects had been very successful, the other was still very much a new work in progress. This from a lab that had been in business for more than three years! Where was the outreach to their colleagues in the business units, and what did this really say about their innovation program?

"Only when the lab is actively engaged with the business units can it realize full potential."

If a lab can't point to users in the business units, how can they possibly be innovating? Yes, I concede there is a tremendous amount of work involved in setting up systems and trying out new tech. Certainly, some of this work would qualify as innovating. That said, if the lab is not operating with, for, or on the behalf of a business unit—solving their real problems or at least better understanding the problem to be solved—where is the innovation? This invisibility is the greatest cause of conflict within the lab space. It is as though the labs are working in isolation from the rest of the organization and are innovating in a vacuum.

Only when the lab is actively engaged with the business units can it realize full potential. It is important for lab heads to note that your digital transformation is designed to complement and enhance the existing intellectual property (IP) of the company—i.e., to allow the IP to reach clients in a new way, or to reimagine a process or procedure, creating internal systems that digitally liberate the firm to operate better. The IP resides not in the innovation lab but in the business units it serves. Without good connections between these critical partners, innovation cannot take hold.

To be fair, there certainly are ample reasons to give innovators their own space within the company. In fact, I am a proponent of segregated innovation zones. It's good to provide innovators a "safe space" to experiment and try new things. It's tough to have colleagues looking over your shoulder critiquing a work in progress, or even worse a project that is likely to fail because it is intentionally bleeding edge. Separation allows them the freedom to try, fail, and try again, the hallmarks of good innovation. What does strike me as odd is why these labs should be relocated miles away from the business units, seemingly to optimize their isolation.

The problem is compounded because the majority of lab employees are new to the industries they are working in. For example, it's rare to find an innovation lab at an insurer that is full of digital experts with an insurance background. They simply don't exist in sufficient quantities. Now, if the labs are invisible and isolated, these younger digital experts will find it extremely difficult, if not impossible, to pick up the industry know-how of seasoned professionals, and more critically the IP that is at the heart of your company. They are not immersed in the business; although digitally competent, they cannot channel this competency through a business-specific filter. This is a recipe for disaster, secluding younger digital experts from the very knowledge they need to succeed, and depriving your business teams of access to a resource that could profoundly improve the way they do business.

Spotting this problem is straightforward if you're a senior executive responsible for overseeing the lab's track record of success. One by one, privately ask your business leaders for the name of the innovation lab head and see if they even know who he or she is and where the lab is. You may be surprised to find the name hard to come by. If they do know the name, the next question is to ask what the lab is currently doing for their team or others. If the lab is invisible they'll have no clue. Now look at this from the other direction and ask your lab head if he or she knows the business unit leader responsible for a specific product or service and see what the response is. It's all part of the same problem. If your lab is invisible the players simply don't know one another. This is your first and most obvious roadblock to attaining meaningful innovation.

From the perspective of the lab manager it's even easier to know if you're invisible. Go to any senior management meeting and see how many people you know by name. If it's only a handful you're behind on your internal marketing, and would do well to sit between two colleagues you've never met and introduce yourself. It may sound trivial, but building your internal network within your company one person at a time is a necessary survival strategy. It will get your name out there and perhaps you'll pick up a few invites for coffee that get you leads on new projects or allies. Same with your team: They represent your lab and need to be tuned into making friends and spreading a positive message.

> *"Remember that if the lab heads think of a project for your team without you—and they will—your voice will be heard second, not first."*

For business unit managers it's even easier still. Chances are you've never met the lab manager, which means it's time for a coffee. Yes, you can wait until that inevitable moment when your team is called in for an innovation project—or, better yet, head it off at the pass to figure out who these lab guys are and what they do. It costs nothing, and might start a more casual discussion that will lead to beneficial projects down the line. Remember that if the lab heads think of a project for your team without you—and they will—your voice will be heard second, not first. If you're already talking with the lab team, you'll get your needs built into the "new idea" on the first go. It will help set a tone and direction from the start that will be in your favour.

There are a number of solutions to help meld innovation labs more tightly into your organization. Reducing the physical separation from the business units is the first and most obvious solution. Clearly this won't work for some companies because of physical space requirements. Still, I suggest that your innovation lab will benefit more acutely from proximity to the business than it will from bean-bag seating strewn on a spacious floor. I've heard the argument that goes something like this: "The cost of space is too expensive to house the innovation lab in our corporate headquarters." To which I reply that the cost of failure to innovate will grossly outweigh any additional expense in rent. As many senior executives are keen to point out, "Innovation is the most important thing we do." If so, treat it as such and bring your innovators closer to your actual business.

Another solution that is easier to effect is absolutely critical: Bring lab personnel into business staff meetings, or have them rotate into the business to work within a specific department for a short period. This is particularly important for younger digital employees who have never worked in your line of business and have no clue as to the actual constraints your business faces. Working closely with execs and team members who actually do the work is critical. Otherwise you run the risk that lab staff will think of their work as an academic exercise (which is understandable given their youth!). This is particularly true for digital employees who work in highly regulated environments like insurance or banking. They commonly feel overwhelmed when their fantastic digital idea meets the hard reality of client data privacy and siloed databases that can't be connected due to regulatory issues. A few weeks at working on the business side will also build bridges and provide mutual insights. Putting a human face on digital innovation may also convert a few of its detractors.

Logically, you can post staff from business into the lab, but here things become trickier. It's likely that your lab runs fairly lean, and the business staffer may feel a bit out of place with little to do, or feel unable to participate in ongoing projects. Clearly you could run a specialized "lab introduction program" but this is a significant undertaking and isn't realistic for all but the largest labs. A creative alternative approach is to run a competition that solicits innovation ideas from your business staff. Attainable ideas could see a temporary posting of the winner to the lab. Together they build out a trial project, which can be transported back to the business for further evaluation. This ensures that employees have a specific role while at the lab, and that the time invested goes into innovations that are actually solving real business problems. This also works to capture IP in your company, since by soliciting input you are really asking what needs to be done to make your company better.

Hackathons for staff are another way of increasing interaction with the laboratory. They are a great way of providing a concentrated multi-day immersive experience that takes a group of business leaders out of their normal jobs to get them thinking about how technology can be used to make their jobs better. What makes these events so powerful is that staff from across the business unit come together and ask fundamental questions about what they do and why they do it. The innovations that come out of these hackathons aren't always technology driven, but may be more oriented to the process and procedures they employ on the job every day. The opportunity to overlay digital technology is simply an added benefit. Hackathons for staff are also a fabulous opportunity for lab personnel to meet one-on-one with their colleagues to teach them how new tech may help them do their jobs better. They can be staged as training events for senior management (who often are the least digital-friendly staff in your company). These events are more common among tech companies but are now working their way into the mainstream. They are a great way to make the lab visible and build bridges between the lab and the business.

Student hackathons, however, have a significantly lower return given the tremendous effort required. In fact, most are just advertisements of corporate largess that serve neither the students' interests nor the sponsoring institution's long-term goals for innovation. It is rare to see a hackathon solution actually adopted by the sponsor since most of the challenge problems are vastly oversimplified. Student hackathons arguably have value as a recruiting tool, but the cost-effectiveness of running an event using the free labor of dozens of young people to find one candidate who may or may not accept your offer is questionable.

A final thought on increasing your lab's visibility is that getting your lab and business personnel together will have unexpected consequences. There will always be hidden talents within your business—like the employee studying coding in his or her spare time, or those with ideas on how to improve what they do but nowhere to go with it. You have tremendous diversity in your staff and you are not using them to their fullest if you don't include them in your innovation plans. Even worse, segregation creates an "us versus them" mentality. Innovation has to be on offer for everyone and creating an inclusive environment is the best way to ensure that it is successfully employed. Imagine the scenario of a disenfranchised employee being told that there is ground-breaking innovation coming to his or her area of expertise. It's hard to imagine this innovation being met with open arms. Curing your lab's invisibility problem will go a long way toward creating an inclusive environment where ideas can be shared and innovation loses its perceived threat.

CALCULATE RETURN ON INVESTMENT

One of the most common complaints I hear coming from lab heads is that they can't get funding for their favorite project. If only the business would understand how important this project is to their long-term well-being and profitability, they'd open the dam and money would come pouring in. When the conversation turns to the potential return on the project, I never cease to be amazed at how many say, "Hey, we're a lab, we don't need ROI." Really?

As an example, I once held a workshop on innovation labs at an innovators conference and had a very engaged audience of around 80 discussing their thoughts on ROI and what it meant for them. In the middle of the discussion, one of the younger participants joined in the discussion and bravely told me that without question his innovation efforts were not held to such banal profitability measures. He went on to say that his innovation efforts would only yield results in five to ten years, and should be judged only on their ability to deliver in that timeframe. I congratulated him on his long-term vision and faith in corporate governance. I then posed this question specifically to older attendees in the audience—those with more extensive experience in corporate governance, "How long does a manager last without profitability in your organization, and how long do managers hang around in general?" The responses were many, swift, and heartfelt. The majority warned their fellow innovator that the general tenure for managers was around two to four years and that profitability, or at least the timeframe in which profitability would be assessed, was closer to two years. This created a rather uncomfortable moment and a look of shock on the innovator with the longer-term view of profitability. While it's always possible that he is blessed with managers and an environment that genuinely rewards long-term innovation, it is more likely that his managers simply hadn't been pressed into thinking about the cost of innovation, and how it would be supported over the long term.

While it is critical that the lab have the freedom to try new technologies, it is equally important that they use ROI as an index or measure to help promote their projects. Labs benefit from the discipline that basic ROI calculations, or other financial metrics, bring with them. It provides a critical link with the other business units, showing the ultimate value of the technology and why investment is required. It also provides something much more important, a common ground over which innovators and business leaders can concentrate and focus their debate. Few business leaders will debate the merits of technology; for most of them this is unknown territory. But give them financial calculations and you can focus their attention and significant experience in debating the funding required. The key is not that the lab gets funded on the first go, but that the lab engages business managers on their home turf and becomes part of the larger discussion on distribution of this critical corporate resource. If a lab isn't engaging here, it will always be looking from the outside in.

The goal of ROI calculations is to provide an unambiguous measure of the project's value and do so in a manner that managers can understand. The issue that is heavily debated within the innovation community is whether dollar value is the only measure that is suitable for use in these calculations, or if soft-money metrics are acceptable. Client-centric metrics like "number of new sales leads" or "number of questions answered" clearly have value, but working these into an ROI calculation takes finesse. Doing a project because it's "the right thing to do" sounds good but is a tough sell. That said, some of the most cutting-edge tech requires this leap of faith.

I recently had a conversation with a successful business innovator that proved this point. He built the first chatbot at his company, which went on to be so successful that it spawned a number of others. To his credit and as a reward for both his vision and success, he was promoted to be the first and only digital officer in his company assigned to a business unit. One of the things he had to overcome with his management team when proposing his new chatbot project was the difficulty in quantifying the dollar value of success. This was brand new technology and it was very hard to put a value on his return calculation, although he was able to show his costs with great detail. He knew intuitively that the chatbot would help answer client questions, thus providing a new means of client-centric engagement, and his challenge was to use finesse in articulating their dollar value in his proposal. Eventually the impasse was broken when managers understood two things. First, the new technology was sufficiently important that if it worked, they could see the benefits of the potential dollar returns he reported. Second, the project cost was sufficiently small that writing it off as a loss would be acceptable. The project essentially advanced as a leap of faith on his ROI calculations, and became immensely profitable in real dollar terms.

"ROI calculations are essentially the fuel for propelling your project ahead."

So the debate is ongoing, but as a practitioner I take little comfort in promoting projects that do not have a direct hard dollar value. It is better to promote a project with a dollar return, even if that return is linked to soft dollar metrics. This is a result of my experience selling innovation in two distinctively different environments. The first, which left a lifelong imprint, was selling the idea of innovation to bankers who wouldn't dream of entertaining a discussion without detailed analysis. The second was selling tech solutions to clients who all needed a clear, hard dollar vision of how a new technology would be worthy of their investment, even if it did not require the detailed plan demanded by the bankers. In both environments, innovation needed an analysis of the return as fuel for moving the transaction forward. That's what ROI calculations essentially are—the fuel for propelling your project and creating a bull's-eye for discussion with management, many of whom have return on resources as their key performance indicator.

Another strong argument is that working in dollars makes you a "player" in your company's future, not just a cost centre. It gives the lab "skin in the game." This is hard for a lot of innovation people to grasp. They often perceive their role as non-combatants, sailing over the day-to-day battles over resources and production in their company. That may be a gift given to the newest of labs, but it will clearly have an expiration date with any changes in management or strategy. While we are certainly in the midst of a massive boom in innovation facilities now, it is impossible to predict how long this will last. Lab managers would be wise to position themselves as potential profit centres rather than cost centres if they seek to build a program that is sustainable and long-lived.

Recognizing this problem within your organization isn't particularly hard. When is the last time you saw an ROI calculation coming out of your innovation team? It doesn't have to be long and rigorous, but is the lab considering this metric and are they bringing it to the table as part of their funding debate? If not, all new proofs-of-concept and outlays for new projects should include an ROI calculation in some form. If you are in a lab you should make these calculations an integral part of your project documentation, even if they haven't been asked for. You'll create an aura of professionalism and show managers that you relate to their world.

There is of course room for flexibility in how ROI is interpreted and presented. If an innovation team slavishly adopts the same calculations and thresholds for profitability as used by business units, things could go badly wrong. Calculating ROI in innovative ways should be encouraged. Lab personnel can be asked to calculate

ROI without specifics as to how, and see what they come up with. Innovative ROI calculation may itself be enlightening for all. I do not suggest making these particularly lengthy or detailed. Tasking the mind of the innovator to account for profitability is a fantastic exercise for all business managers. Some of the calculations may be based on wishful thinking, and that's fine. The more educated guesses will derive from cognates used by your competition, or from prior experience applying similar tech. Both will be highly educational. Innovators are tremendously resourceful in finding answers when they have to.

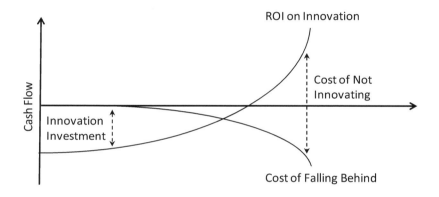

Calculating the ROI on innovation captures only part of the story. The cost of falling behind the competiton is rarely considered and leads to underestimating the true costs of not innovating.

That innovation should be held to a different profitability standard than an existing business unit is without question. There are three main reasons why. First, it is an investment made today that we only recover tomorrow. Second, there are nonobvious assumptions that come into play; we need to factor the true cost of *not* innovating. Innovation expert Clayton M. Christensen pointed out the flaw in comparing the cost of innovation to a static view of the company's future performance. In this static view doing nothing will not have a cost on company performance, while in reality it does. Third, many funded projects will simply fail. For these reasons, locking an innovation lab into a company standard of calculating ROI will stifle innovation and provide a barrier for entry that simply may be too high for new tech to overcome. At the same time, a lab that doesn't calculate ROI at all, ever, has no long-term vision of how its work sustains the company. Optimal and long-lived innovation needs financial discipline.

FOCUS ON PEOPLE, NOT TECH

I have news for you. Your innovation lab's biggest job is not bringing in new technology, it's breaking down barriers erected by your employees and clients to using it. Note that we are talking about two distinct constituencies. It's not enough to repeat Amazon's mantra that digital has to help you become the "Earth's most customer-centric company." That sounds great and is a laudable goal. But if your innovation lab isn't focused on their fellow colleagues in addition to the customers, they're falling down on their primary mission, which is to make your people receptive to new technology and the changes it brings.

> *"It's not enough to repeat Amazon's mantra that digital has to help you become the 'Earth's most customer-centric company.'"*

Innovation isn't about the tech, but instead the relation of people to tech. Note: this is the opposite of what you're being sold by tech companies on a daily basis. The general pitch that you see in the media is that if you adopt some new plug-in technology your problems will all be solved. Put blockchain on this system and you'll reap tremendous rewards, use AI on that one and your problems will all go away. We've heard it before, but for some reason we are happy to be fooled once more.

Why do we consistently fall for the message that tech will solve our problems? In short because we all wish it would work as advertised. Systems are easier to deal with than people, so at some level we are victims of our own desire for a magical outcome. You can't blame us for wishful thinking, but at the same time we must take some responsibility for ignoring the obvious. People use tech, adopt tech, fight tech and cause either its success or demise. If someone actually took the time to talk to a customer service person about the brand new shiny chatbot that will augment their department, they would find very little enthusiasm indeed. The service agent's first thought is "How much longer will I have my job if an AI-driven chatbot is doing some of my work?" Given this, their second thought may well be how they can delay or derail the project. Again, this has nothing to do with the quality or viability of the tech, and everything to do with the people surrounding it.

Many organisations with innovation labs believe that their primary responsibility is to capture and master whatever new tech will benefit the company. This partial approach is a sure road to innovation lab failure. Technology unto itself will not change your organization if your staff are not open and willing to accept the transformation. This message is gradually sinking in and a number of high-profile companies have implemented special training programs to increase employees' willingness to accept digital adoption. Innovation labs must be on the front lines of this effort.

One of the opening lines I use with banking audiences is to tell them that they don't work for a bank but a tech company. It usually gets good laughs. When I use the exact same line at the end of my lecture, usually no one laughs. During the course of my talk I demonstrate how technology is changing their industry with real examples currently deployed at their competitors. When no one laughs at the end of the lecture I know I've done my job. They grasp the importance of tech in their industry, and maybe are slightly more willing to embrace it because they see how important it is to their own survival.

One of the superstars amid our current technologies is blockchain. Without question it's on top of everyone's list as the system that can change everything. I've seen countless labs run blockchain proof of concepts (POCs) to educate the lab staff on the intricacies of its implementation. In the vast majority of these cases, they barely spoke to the compliance or operations staff, and these personnel were rarely if ever included in the POC. Yet these two groups are those most affected by blockchain's claims of a paperless back office, and are the end owners of blockchain's labors. Is the lab doing a good job with blockchain by running the POC and getting a jump on the technology, or would it have been better for the company to have a long hard sit-down with the operations team and spending the same resources training them first? The answer is easy. Technical mastery of blockchain by the innovation lab team will have absolutely zero impact on compliance's or operations' willingness to accept this tech. To compound the problem, in the end the innovation team will likely not implement the tech themselves but will purchase a solution and work with partners from the marketplace.

Clearly, the innovation lab needs to understand technology and run POCs that benefit the company. Obviously, a lab isn't filled with Luddites; tech is their deal. All the same, mastering tech at the expense of mastering people will slow and delay the innovation process. The people in the business units will be the end arbiters of tech's failure or success. They bear your company's IP and without their buy-in your tech platform will struggle. Ensuring that resources are spent training and enabling them are certainly better allocated than training your lab team to become world-class technical masters of a solution, except of course in the rare case where your lab really does need to build a solution from scratch.

The telltale signs of this problem are potentially subtler than some of the others we've discussed. If your lab is training to master a technology to a high level, it's laudable and should be supported. Likewise vetting new tech to see if it meets minimum expectations.

This is, in part, what they're there for. What you need to interrogate is the degree of connectivity with the rest of your company. Apart from the two examples above, working in isolation is not a good sign.

To this end, the lab should be encouraged to produce a plan/timeline for implementation of all tech projects into the business units. Then they should back it up by having introductory sessions with managers and staff. This serves a two-fold purpose. First, it begins the process of acclimating staff to new digital products. You'll know that the team is really doing their job if the first technical sessions have a few people attending who either don't know why they are there, or feel that they should be somewhere else. Initial meetings will make your non-tech staff feel a sense of inclusion and help get the message across to everyone that innovation is important. The second purpose is to start the "collaborative process" that is so critical to innovation. Unless your lab and business units collaborate, your innovation program won't go anywhere. These introductory meetings will be the glue that holds these groups together. The lab staff will learn a tremendous amount from the business unit and come away with a more refined approach to applying the tech. Your other staff will feel included and respected for their contributions to your company's IP.

One thing that is clear is that it's very easy for labs to get caught in this self-destructive behavior of believing that tech alone will solve the problem. Remember that it's easier to show progress in mastering technology than mastering people and culture. It is the path of least resistance. Your lab's number one priority, therefore, is to work with your staff and clients to get them ready and willing to accept change. This is a hard message and may be troublesome for some in your lab. Lab people love tech and that's a good thing. Interacting more with people and less with screens may not come naturally, but it's in the best interest of all involved.

BEST PRACTICE

4

SAY NO TO CARTE BLANCHE

E very innovation lab wants freedom and I certainly understand why. From the lab's perspective, the more freedom they have the greater the range of innovation they can bring to the parent. We have all been warned to "be careful what you wish for" and it is the same with innovation labs. Having full freedom to innovate sounds great, but the lack of focus may delay delivering usable results to the business.

The whole idea of bringing in an innovation team is to get them thinking about your business problems in a new way and bring technology to bear. You want this to happen in the broadest sense and the lab should feel unconstrained in its ability to create innovation in areas that initially appear out of the norm. That said, loose boundaries are useful to help guide the direction of innovation taking place at your lab. This is especially true of younger teams that have never worked in your industry. Assuming that they can somehow anticipate the issues faced by the rest of your staff is overly optimistic.

Here are mission statements for several leading innovation labs:

- Liberty Mutual, Solaria Labs: "to bring disruptive innovations that make a better, safer future"
- MetLife, LumenLab: "applies a thoughtful, structured, and methodical process to incubating ideas, and developing new businesses that can scale."
- DBS, Asia X (DAX): "is a space where we collaborate with start-ups and the broader FinTech community to reimagine, inspire and create the future of innovation."
- Expedia: "Transforming travel in Asia"
- ManuLife, Lab of Forward Thinking (LOFT): "explores emerging technologies, new business processes and consumer needs to deliver innovative solutions."
- Ikea, SPACE10: "The purpose of SPACE10 is to enable a better, more meaningful and sustainable life for many people. We are on a mission to explore and design new ways of living."
- Alphabet, "X": "We create radical new technologies to solve some of the world's hardest problems."

It interesting to see the heady goals of these mission statements. That they are inspirational and quite broad is no surprise; what is noteworthy is which of them reference real business objectives. Only one, from LumenLab, cites building businesses as a goal. Clearly these statements have no relationship to the level of innovation coming out of these facilities, and this is not to suggest any of the labs have underperformed. But it's interesting that only one pays lip service to building businesses, which is, for every other division in all these companies, the mantra. In an earlier chapter I mentioned that innovation labs are typically invisible to fellow employees. Given that most have such broad-ranging missions, which include everything *but* building a business, it's easy to see why.

"Carte blanche" innovation lends itself to many outcomes that are, to put it kindly, obscure or oblique. One example comes from a lab in the financial sector. They built a social connections site that matches people with similar needs. Web traffic analysis for the site shows an Alexa traffic rank in the high millions (i.e., low traffic) and Facebook likes in the low hundreds after a year and a half of service. While the site is certainly professionally done, one has to wonder about its value to the parent and, more importantly, what the lab learned that will make it better at its mission in the future. That it appears to have failed to catch on with users isn't the main issue; in fact I applaud and readily accept any failure in innovation almost as much as I do successes. The bigger question is how does this app fit into the company's agenda? An argument always can be made that skills or techniques were developed that serve the company in some significant manner, but one has to wonder why this site was generated in the first place if it does not promote the lab's company in any meaningful way, shows no apparent mastery of new technology, and doesn't appear to support their clients or product. It's a nice idea, but it was built with the earnings of others in the business units and apparently did not contribute to furthering the parent's objectives. Carte blanche? We can't know for sure, but yes, I believe so.

> *"I understand if lab people reading this are not pleased with my assessment that excessive freedom can be a problem."*

I understand if lab people reading this are not pleased with my assessment that excessive freedom can be a problem with innovation labs. The presumption of freedom is why they went into innovation in the first place, and it is rightly dear to them. I am not suggesting that labs be put under the boot of constraints that compels innovation in one direction only. What I will say is that some limitations can prove liberating. Bach and Mozart were geniuses but composed within the framework of what constituted acceptable music in their time. In many ways they were significantly constrained as to the form music could take, especially when compared to later generations of composers. In like fashion, innovation teams need to work within the structure of real business constraints in order to be effective.

It's easy to determine if your lab is suffering from too much freedom. Like a pet cat that politely deposits a dead bird on your doorstep in gratitude for your love, innovation labs can do the same. If their projects are off the mark—i.e., if they do not support your brand, your clients, or your business units, do not resonate with other company objectives or strategies—perhaps it's time to reset the boundaries and refocus engagement. At issue isn't the project's success or failure, or the tech it uses, but the direction in which it's heading.

Rewriting a mission statement may be a start, but will not provide your innovation lab the redirection required to get it back on track. The best redirection comes from problem solving from within. Perform a reset by asking the lab to contribute solutions to real business problems posed by your managers. In the best of worlds your business heads will be looking for assistance, which will make for an easy marriage. Another way to get innovation back on track may be the aforementioned employee hackathons, or another activity that forces the lab to fix, solve or engage the real problems faced by the business.

I have seen a number of newer labs given "carte blanche" to innovate as they see fit. It didn't last long; invariably the lab was given some gentle redirection. Too many dead birds were laid at management's doorstep. Not the fault of the innovation team, for how can they meet with management's expectations when those expectations have not been clearly delineated?

BALANCE STAFFING

Staffing innovation labs is painful. Hiring a group of twenty-somethings with impressive digital credentials isn't easy, as they are in short supply and highly sought after. But that isn't the hard part. Even harder is getting them to understand your business and providing oversight by someone attuned to the industry and your company's needs.

There are two opposing tendencies that have equally bad results if pursued to the extreme. The first is to hire an innovation team with domain expertise. The most common expression of this is to simply take a number of people out of your IT or other departments and rebrand them innovators. These are colleagues who have worked in the industry for at least a few years, seen how the business is done, and bring a wealth of knowledge. The problem is that most lack the ability to span the digital divide from tech implementation to innovation. There are undoubtedly some out there, but they are rare. In most cases industry insiders—from IT or from other business groups—come laden with notions of how business should be done, simply because they grew up with it and are uncomfortable challenging established practice. In addition, innovation has not been a metric for success in their career, so asking them to suddenly be creative—take their mind "off task"—will be a rough transition.

One lab thought they made the right choice when they pulled an industry veteran from within their ranks to head their new lab. He came with a fine pedigree and had headed some of the company's core business units. He had a long and distinguished career in the industry and was widely seen as an expert. It was a logical choice, given that he was experienced, had some tech exposure and certainly would support the goals of parent. They bought all of the right furniture, had the inspirational murals on the wall as well as the Italian coffee machine prized by so many innovation teams. The grand opening took place and the innovation was set to begin. On closer inspection the scene had an interesting incongruity that might have foreshadowed what was to come. Among the jeans-and-T-shirt-clad twenty-somethings was the new innovation lab head, an older gentleman wearing a suit and tie. At face value I detected that something was amiss. Within two years the lab was looking for a replacement chief amid suggestions that it was grossly underperforming and the young staff were not happy. All of this because of a tie? No of course not, there were other factors involved, but it serves as a metaphor for how extremely difficult it is for existing staff to make the leap to the innovation business. There is a message being sent by the hundreds of innovation labs formed in recent years: innovation is a distinct business sector. It has KPIs, methodologies and protocols that must be understood for success to ensue. An existing employee can't simply be tossed in and told to wing it.

> *"It's not enough to set digitally sophisticated innovators loose in your business."*

The preponderance of twenty-somethings that populate most labs is to be expected, given the generation gap in digital skills. This is where the second tendency leading to bad results comes into play—one that was discussed in detail in Chapter 5 "Best Practice

1: Visibility." Young people won't have a good grip on the industry, your company, and your specific business concerns. It's not enough to set digitally sophisticated innovators loose in your business with the thought that they can change anything and everything. They need guidance and contact with people who understand the business, its systems and limitations imposed by legal and other regulation. For all their energy, young people have another problem: they actually believe the mission statements that say they can achieve anything. Imagine the reality that kicks in when they first visit the compliance department, or worse, the compliance department's reaction when they see their latest digital solution.

A pair of hipster innovators from a local lab came to my lab one day for a chat over coffee. We took a seat on our comfy couch and gazed out on Singapore's Marina Bay from a glorious 50th story view. I noticed that they appeared a bit down so I asked why. One was a blockchain coder of some local fame, the other an idea guy lacking an innate attention to details. They were dejected because their company was unwilling to accept the blockchain solution that the two had personally devised for their business. I asked for more details as to the design and implementation. It turns out they planned for it to be built internally, by them. Sensing the huge scope of the task I began gently probing around the edges to see if they had hired consultants and software vendors (which might provide an opportunity for my own team if the project were later resuscitated). The answer was no, they hadn't engaged any additional technical support, had no money to do so, and were going to make a go of it alone. Needless to say I was stunned, though I did commiserate with their sense of betrayal when the project was nixed. Changing the subject to the more technical aspects of the project, it turns out that it would have required a major overhaul of the company's internal processes.

For approval, the pair had gone to the lab and regional business heads, who told them flat out that the institution wasn't ready for that degree of disruption, bootstrapped no less. Surprise! Typically, a project of this magnitude wouldn't budge in any major corporation without serious expenditures for consultants, systems integrators and software vendors like IBM. While I salute the team's confidence in their capabilities and their *chutzpah* in proposing such an ambitious project, it is hard to square their youthful exuberance with the realities of undertaking a major systems overhaul at a large corporation. This is a classic case of young innovators taking a company at its word and delivering innovation, meanwhile lacking any guidance on what and how much to innovate, and, hardest of all, how to get innovation through "the system."

This scenario is repeated hundreds of times a day in my industry. Young people have been told they should be as "out there" as possible, only to run into the reality that deems parts of the business sacred or untouchable. Without some coaching ahead of time, or training as to what and how business is done, young lab employees will become disillusioned and frankly disenfranchised. They tune out after hearing "no" too many times and start wishing that they worked for Google or Amazon.

How to avoid this scenario? Bring your lab employees up to speed on what your business does. The best training takes the form of temporary postings to business units, so that they see how business is conducted and make contacts within the broader company. It helps to increase lab visibility and gets your team familiar with the business constraints that you live under. An added bonus is that they will spread the word of digital within your organization and plant a few seeds that may grow into real innovation projects in the future.

Another method is via on-site training. With my own team, I found the easiest way to get their heads around finance was to provide a series of lectures that explained what our various clients do, how they fit in the financial system, and what tech might do for them. My team was very digitally sophisticated and could provide the tech element in fintech, but were blind to how the tech could be used because they had only a rudimentary understanding of what financial institutions do. Closing this gap enabled them to better serve clients because they could now imagine how their tech fit into financial institutions.

It can be difficult to avoid an overemphasis on digital skills within your lab. A way to combat this is to implant a few carefully selected team members out of the business units into the lab. This is a great way to get business savvy into the team and provides a direct link to the business. In addition, it reduces the internal tensions set up by an "us versus them" mentality. Deploying traditional employees to break down barriers should improve both the quality of projects and their acceptance by business units.

As always, the devil is in the details. One financial institution transferred a large number of staff out of the IT department into their newly formed lab unit. To no one's surprise, attrition was high. The first and most obvious problem was that having IT skills does not translate to either the desire to become an innovator or the innate ability to do so effectively. IT is not akin to innovation, even though they have computers in common. In fact, the best IT personnel may be thoroughly rigid thinkers. Anyway, to compound the indignity, the transfer was perceived by many as the first step in their eventual termination, even though this wasn't management's intent. So good talent was lost to the market, and the negative energy created was damaging to everyone.

You can be sure you have this problem if your twenty-somethings begin leaving for other jobs. The trick is to step in before your lab team gets disillusioned. This is critical if, like most labs, you are heavily weighted toward younger employees. Take a look at the innovations that they're working on or have proposed. What's the success rate? If you're looking at low implementation, dig into understanding why, and push a few of the better projects through to completion. This helps the lab feel that it is contributing and is relevant. I guarantee that your lab team genuinely wants to help, and derives its sense of worth from contributing. If there is nothing on the agenda that makes sense, your lab has had too much "carte blanche." It is underperforming due to a lack of direction guiding the youthful exuberance.

Striking a balance between youth and experience is like walking a tightrope. When the BUs say that the lab "doesn't get that we just can't do that" or the lab employees say, "We could do so much more if they'd let us do our job," there's your reliable indicator that the equilibrium is skewed.

AVOID THE BIG PLAN

Innovation is like the game of poker. You shouldn't expect to play a single large hand and win. Instead, you gain bit by bit over many smaller hands as you accrue knowledge about your opponents; you may even lose a few hands toward the greater goal. Innovation labs aren't much different.

I have seen more than a few working "the big hand." Their plans are large, all-encompassing, and suck up the bulk of the lab team's energy and efforts. These projects "will change everything," having a significant impact on the sponsoring company's operations. Labs in this position are betting heavily on a single outcome, playing single hands of high-stakes poker in a casino where, guess what, the tables are rigged.

A much better tactic is to get to work on a series of small but achievable innovation goals that allow the lab to show consistent but incremental progress. Why? Because in the end, the lab will be measured by *what it has achieved*. Even if none of these achievements are a breakthrough, they indicate that progress is underway. In most corporate settings this metric is critical. Going back to the last paragraph, why do I claim that the casino is rigged? It's very simple. Top management is by nature results-driven. Patience has its limits, even if that's not apparent in day-to-day operations. Changes in personnel, strategy, or the company's financial outlook can change everything. One day the music may stop. When it does the laboratory is in a much better position to defend its right to exist if it can point to measurable wins, no matter what the size, throughout the company.

Another reason small wins win is that this mindset feeds agility. The lab can potentially leap from one division to another to introduce a new and easily digested solution. This proves the lab's worth, converts detractors, spreads the message of digitization, and become ingrained in the operations of the company. Realistically this isn't always possible, and it's important to acknowledge that some of the problems to be solved just may be too big. But every venture out of the lab and into wider world down the halls provides an opportunity show off the lab's skills and win deep-seated support.

Achieving small wins can be its own goal, whether or not the technology or idea implemented is, in fact, disruptive. It's not a zero-sum game. Striving for incremental gains doesn't relegate the lab to working on less-than-sexy tech in perpetuity, or signal a surrender to implementing well needed disruption on a larger scale. Small wins simply position the lab to show that continuous progress is being made and to signal that the disruption may well be coming.

To show the contrast between "the big plan" and small wins I'm going to examine two technologies that exemplify these extremes. Both are used heavily by innovation labs and represent cutting-edge implementations. The two technologies are AI-based chatbots and blockchain. What makes them interesting is that they are in the news every day and no lab would be complete without them.

Chatbots are extremely popular and you can find them just about anywhere on the web (notably your bank's homepage). Why? One reason is that even though they are relatively new technology, they are relatively straightforward to implement. Chatbots are commonly used to improve customer service and are in general useful as part of every company's AI strategy. Another, hidden reason is that innovation labs know that chatbots are a quick win. Smart labs looking for quick wins know from others' experience that the technology is no longer "bleeding edge." It can be put to work relatively quickly and with good results to deliver an all-important win that highlights their prowess. This is a great example of technology that helps unify the labs and the business units.

Now let's look at blockchain. How many blockchain applications do you see up and running? There are a few, but the technical difficulties make it my favorite example of "the big plan." Many labs have entire teams dedicated to transforming their institution with blockchain. Worse, they are going to build the blockchain applications in-house without guidance from outside experts. Does this sound grandiose? It is—equivalent to high-stakes poker on a rigged table. Rigged because while that the lab is working on its "big plan" it is invisible to the rest of the company, and less and less relevant to their growth. In addition, whereas chatbot technology unifies the lab and the business units, blockchain generally disrupts, driving a wedge between the lab and business.

"Oftentimes labs with "the big plan" are heavily tech-centric rather than people-centric."

Now, I love both technologies; please do not presume that I hate blockchain, as nothing could be further from the truth. But it's important to see its implementation in the context of labs, and what can be realistically achieved with these disparate technologies. Blockchain will one day change how we do business, and your lab is the perfect place to explore it, but do you want to bet the house with time and money spent exploring?

Oftentimes labs with "the big plan" are heavily tech-centric rather than people-centric, as discussed in an earlier chapter. This is not a slight on their commitment—the lab staffers work long hours, are genuinely engaged, and in their own view are extremely productive. Meanwhile, the rest of their colleagues wonder what on earth they are up to.

You'll know this is a problem for your lab if the promised grand initiative never seems to arrive, needing 'just a bit more work' before it's ready for roll out. Letting this continue unchallenged is a problem. Delays are inevitable in working life, but good managers seek to understand the cause. Is it because the innovation is too expansive, difficult or ambitious? It's reasonable to ask for a demonstration of the prototype, to judge for yourself the rate of progress. This is where things get difficult because only your lab staff truly understand the technology and it may be necessary to get some external confirmation that your lab team is proceeding effectively if they are developing the tech in-house. External validation can come from a host of sources; your existing consultants and IT companies will gladly send out a few experts if they smell a potential extension to the existing engagements with your company. The best advice, however, will come from young upstart independent tech providers working in the same space that are angling for a new client. They will provide insight into your lab's progress and perhaps suggest ways to make it even better. While this is underway, check the schedule for future work. If there are other projects that are relatively easy to achieve, move them immediately to the top of the list.

Let's face it, the lab environment is not conducive to self-reflection: it is hard for them to see that they are stuck, or worse, limiting their prospects by continuing on a large project. It's easy to bite off far more than they can chew in terms of technology adoption and delivery. Blockchain is always the best example. The technology may appear manageable at first, but the deeper you go the more unwieldy and complicated it becomes. Once in the middle of any big project, the sunk cost of time and energy makes it increasingly painful to admit failure. Despite the innovators' mantra to "fail fast" it's often very difficult to realize in practice. Completing smaller, more easily attainable projects with moderate ROIs can compensate the pain of suspending or delaying the big plan.

To get your lab redirected onto smaller, attainable projects, a two-pronged deployment of carrot-and-stick may have the best ultimate outcome. Can funds be released to hire a vendor who can assist the lab in getting an easy win? This external assistance is the carrot—the stick being a temporary freeze on the lab's other projects, pending a real goal attained. This will sweeten the imposition of discipline and redirection that otherwise might leave staff demoralized and feeling misunderstood. Pulling them off the project without the carrot might be viewed as a lack of faith in their abilities.

Most companies have limited patience waiting for the "big win," which can convey a general sense within the ranks that the lab is irrelevant or window dressing. I've seen a lot of innovations operations betting heavily on the "one big project" that will put the lab on its feet and win respect from the BUs. The better path is to consistently put together small wins that show consistent forward motion. If a lab is distracted and flailing with an overambitious goal, help snap them out of what amounts to a death spiral. Even if it creates a bit of friction at the outset, everyone benefits in the long term.

BUY DON'T BUILD

I never cease to be amazed at the number of labs trying to build technology internally, when acquiring it from external vendors is faster, cheaper, and results in better quality. I understand the natural pride that one gets from accomplishing a "do it yourself" (DIY) project at home or on the job. I also acknowledge there may be tech requirements that are so highly specific that building it yourself is the only path. That said, technology adoption is not the same as putting up new wallpaper. Professional developers spend thousands of hours thinking about the best way to solve problems and develop solutions—hours that your lab teams would never be able to duplicate. Bringing their solutions onboard can give your company a significant head start and do so for a pittance compared to sinking those hours themselves.

I met for coffee with a lab employee of a global financial company that had a relatively modest innovation team in place. We chatted about their projects and he eventually mentioned that they were building a chatbot. Given that I was also building one for a client, I asked whose AI engine they were using. (A brief technical digression: the AI engine is the part that understands language.

All of the large software providers and some of the smaller and/or open-source vendors provide them pre-built.) His response shocked me to the point I spilled my coffee. He said that they were building the underlying engine themselves. Seeing my spilt coffee and incredulity, he said this was 100% acceptable to his management, because they thought it appropriate that the lab should master this technology. I sipped what was left and sighed. My chatbot project was up and working within months; I still haven't seen his financial company's chatbot at work.

All of our companies are technology users. We have email programs, web browsers, accounting systems, servers and even cloud-based services. All of this is bought from external vendors who have entire teams that spend tens of thousands of man hours to refine and develop these products. Why is innovation any different? Let's grant that in some cases a unique solution may be required, usually because of specialized system requirements that can't be bought on the open market. In most cases however, what your innovation lab is trying to accomplish is new to your company, but not new to the marketplace. There are myriad start-up software and tech providers out there who have already tried, failed, and tried again in countless iterations to overcome the very problem you are up against. Why not use them to your full advantage?

> *"In most cases, what your innovation lab is trying to accomplish is new to your company, but not new to the marketplace."*

I imagine this observation will leave some lab people seething, so let me clarify. Unless you work for one of the major tech providers, most of what we try to achieve in our innovation labs with digital technology has been done before. Maybe not for the same use parameters, or within the same system framework. Maybe your competitors are unaware it exists. All the same, someone somewhere has implemented a system with similar intent. An innovation team's resources shouldn't be wasted on "reinventing the wheel," which means purchasing as much pre-built technology as possible given that it can be made to fit within system and functional requirements. A valid exception is the case where a lab opts to build prototypes to educate themselves and gain expertise on a new technology, to help them make a better decision on what to buy.

Getting back to the scene with the lab employee above, I doubt that the financial institution in question would try to build versions of Microsoft Word or Excel, so why build a chatbot from scratch? Even more curious is why the lab manager thinks that building a chatbot engine would be in the best interests of his young, small team. Wouldn't they be better served by implementing an existing solution and actually getting a functioning chatbot up many months earlier? Another issue is that having invested time and money in training his staff to build from scratch, how will this knowledge be passed on within the organization? Young people are mobile, and these skills are likely to be lost when they move on to other employers.

"Your team's goal is to be the provider of innovation and not necessarily the builder."

Your lab team takes tremendous pride in its work and needs to understand how tech works. It is critical that they have a firm understanding of how to apply and build with a new technology before plugging it in to solving a problem. As mentioned previously, if their expertise is improved by formulating and experimenting with trial technology, this makes perfect sense. In the end, however, your team's goal is to be the *provider* of innovation and not necessarily the *builder*. Building is long and tedious; ask anyone who works in the software business. More importantly, it takes a tremendous time investment to build sufficiently robust production-level solutions. Your lab team should only attempt to do this with clear justification.

Where your innovation lab can truly excel is to be the greatest implementers of technology in your company. Implement means making technology work for you by getting fully functioning digital assets up and running on your systems. Your lab should strive to break internal records for how fast they can evaluate, apply, configure, purchase and adopt new tech. They should know your system requirements and be able to work with third-party vendors large and small to test and evaluate how new technology can solve your business problems. This alone is a significant undertaking and will take quite a while for a new lab team to achieve. By doing this they will bring more innovation into your company faster and cheaper.

Earlier I stated that buying tech was faster, cheaper, and in many cases better. Let's look at these claims one at a time. Imagine a hypothetical where your lab team wants to build software that is also available on the open market, from a young start-up company. This assumption is reasonable since start-ups are often working on the same kinds of new tech your lab will be interested in. First and foremost, cheaper: the cost basis for your team to build new tech easily exceeds that of the start-up, whose low pay/high share ownership gives them some of the cheapest development costs to be found anywhere. Faster is obvious. If a solution is already available, it can be deployed almost immediately. Now the hard one—will it be better? If your innovation team has been thinking about a problem for six months, and the tech provider has been in business for two years, it's a likely bet they have an 18-month advantage over your innovation team. In addition, with no disrespect intended, it's unlikely that your innovation team can beat a start-up run by four equivalent twenty-somethings at their own game. The start-up has been purposefully assembled to do one specific task. Your company can profit from their laser-like focus.

You should already know if your innovation team is building products on their own, and whether there is a compelling reason for them to do so. If not, it's time to find out. You've got to take a look at exactly what they're building and whether it can be sourced on the open market. Ask why they're building rather than buying, and for a comparison of features with what's available in the marketplace. Is it cost effective for them to build and is it the most efficient way to deliver innovation? There are a lot of reasons why building may be the right path. Mitigating factors may be cost or simply something so basic as the obscure tech provider that they wanted to buy from couldn't help them. It happens.

If your lab team is building their own technology because they have no budget to purchase the services of a third-party software or tech provider, it's time to take a good look at your innovation program. If you've assembled the people, rented the space and bought espresso machines but have not provided a budget to purchase outside tech, something is wrong. If your vision is that the ideal innovation lab builds its own tech, I hope that my arguments against this can convince you. If this situation exists because there is simply no money left, then the only solution is to hit up the business units for additional funds for projects relevant to their needs. I don't have to tell you that this won't be easy.

USE DISCIPLINED PROJECT MANAGEMENT

Innovation loathes a timeline. No matter how we try to put it on a schedule or speed results through agile delivery and "failing fast," it doesn't always go according to plan. Your lab won't have fresh product to roll out on a predictable basis. Holding to a schedule will be next to impossible and planning innovation launches to coincide with visits by investors is fraught with peril. Much of what these staffers are doing is new, untested, and unproven. It's likely that setbacks and delays are the norm.

Project management is a key discipline for your innovation lab to learn, and is critical to harnessing an admittedly difficult and complicated process. Perhaps because I've been an innovator, I am sympathetic to labs doing this work. Projects come off the tracks for a lot of reasons, which oftentimes have nothing to do with the tech itself. The key to managing innovation projects is knowing how much delay is tolerable, how to manage it and the expectations that go with it, and hardest of all, when to call it quits.

A client of mine was nearing the end of a six-month software project. They launched phase one of an innovative new digital sales campaign on their website. The software was a major step forward both for the company and the marketplace because it offered services on-line that had not been available before in the Singapore market. It was innovative software. Pushing the developer and small in-house tech team to deliver was a real challenge, but they got it done. Or so they thought.

The software developer had never built this type of product before and was truly challenged with how best to modify their existing software product to capture a new type of business that was related t0, but not quite the same as, what their product was designed for. They were innovating in the best sense of the word, not altogether differently from how your lab might. They had systems that worked beautifully for one use case, and these could reasonably be adapted to another. The problem was, the developer needed to embed new technology in order to make it all work. The system was launched. What followed holds lessons for innovators everywhere. After the launch, new bugs were discovered that had not been caught during testing. It turns out that the problems that surfaced were not evident in the on-line marketplace portion of the solution that lent itself to easy testing. The problems were deeply embedded in calculation algorithms that when tested individually produced correct results but were not correctly aggregated in the finished code.

"Innovators are by nature optimists and the solution is always just around the corner."

Teams were assembled to correct problems, make revisions, and deliver a functioning product. Work around the clock in multiple time zones progressed at breakneck speed while bug after bug was fixed, but like the game of "whack-a-mole" new ones steadily appeared. Every fix was met with the promise that it would be the last, until one week of revisions became four. Finally, the buyer came in and pulled the plug on the entire development effort. I watched the developer desperately plea to keep his project alive.

It was a memorable moment and needless to say, legal teams on both sides were deployed. The first moral of the story is that there is a point when you have to make hard calls with innovation projects. Innovators like developers are by nature optimists and the solution is always just around the corner, but at some point we all run out of corners. The second moral to the story would be to thoroughly test the code, and this clearly was not done to sufficient depth with this product. The marketplace-facing code was checked ad nauseam, while the mundane calculations that took place in the back office were checked with trials that were overly simplistic and did not catch the embedded errors.

Innovation projects do have lives of their own and shouldn't be subject to the same rules as a project coming out of your IT department. Here's the difference. When we start an IT project we know exactly what we want to achieve, which resources we will use, and what technology we're going to deploy to get the job done. Timing, schedules, and costs flow logically from these known quantities. What we want the technology to do is usually guaranteed to occur, because it's been done before by the very teams that we hire to do the job. What's more, each person on that team has a clearly delineated role.

In contrast, we often start an innovation project with only an approximate concept of what we'd like to achieve. If we get there, great. If we arrive at a different result, it may still have value. Innovation is rarely linear. In most but not all cases, innovation isn't about delivering a fixed product; it's about delivering incremental improvements in a process or interface using new technologies. The precise result is rarely obvious at the outset, given that the technology we are applying is usually untested and the users are often inexperienced in its implementation.

For example, it's very popular to use artificial intelligence to read insurance claims forms. AI can read the medical procedures or car repair amounts charged to see if the numbers make sense. The obvious problem is how well does the AI read and to what level will the AI assist humans in this work. Frankly, no one can know until the project is underway, the AI is trained, and some preliminary results obtained. Perhaps someday AI will do this work with such perfection that humans won't be part of the process, but certainly in the early stages AI will make a lot of mistakes and need lots of hands-on attention. Moreover, real world use may reveal ways in which the AI might be deployed that were not initially predicted. For example, should it search for outliers in claims amounts that are then flagged and turned over to human processing? Or is it preferable to focus the AI on "normal" claims, thereby reducing the need for human intervention in the vast majority of instances? Neither of these questions can be answered until you build and test the system's responses.

The resources we need to deliver innovation projects are even more variable, because they depend at least in part on the technology we will be using. If you're experimenting with new technology it may not be clear at the outset which is best. I watched analytics projects in my own team flip back and forth between R and Python many times over before they settled on the tool that best suited the project's needs. To make matters worse, whatever tech the project will be using is often being tested for the first time, so the lab team really doesn't know if it will work as advertised. Using traditional project management techniques to try to cost and schedule a project with these attributes is quite challenging.

Why don't innovation projects work toward a fixed objective or outcome? Because in most cases, innovators work not only with goals, but with technology that will need tweaking to be a good fit. They are wrestling with variables that are really out of their direct control and they can't know the outcome until they test the technology. Say a sales division needs a chatbot. It's not as simple as the lab team delivering a chatbot; they first need to determine things like the level of conversation it can achieve, and which vendor's AI engine delivers fastest, easiest, and at what price. These are grey areas of tech that you run up against before you've even discussed what the user interface will look like. Many factors need to align to keep an innovation project on track.

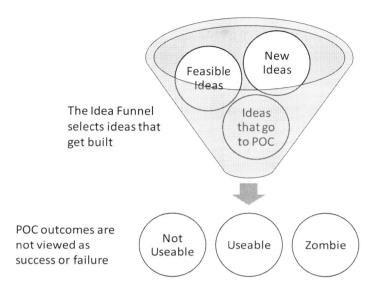

Innovation ideas will go through a funnel and only a few will make it to Proof of Concept (POC.) Post-POC projects will be judged useful or not. There is a third category of projects that stick around as "undead" zombies.

In the real world, most projects fall behind. Wrestling with new technology is the cause of many delays. Even worse is when an unruly innovation project bolts the lab thanks to premature implementation and needs time out for debugging, which is a more public and inglorious failure. Equally bad are projects that languish in the lab for ages, despite the innovator's mantra of "fail fast." They become what I call zombie projects. No matter how long they limp along they never seem to die a natural death.

I know you've seen them too, but you may never have thought of them in this way. If your lab is giving shelter to some technology that looked hot, new, and full of promise six months ago, but is still only in demo form without any advances, you just might have a zombie project on your hands. If it's simply an old project used for demos, that's fine, we all do this. The important question is whether this project is actively consuming resources and just keeps trudging along as though it's on life support. Killing off zombie projects is humane.

Innovation teams' natural and commendable state of optimism make them loathe to kill off projects. A big break is always just around the corner, in the form of a technological breakthrough or a business unit that will bestow money on the project to get it working. Sometimes zombie projects become like pets, trotted out during innovation open houses as proof that people are busy and all is well. It's tough to kill them off internally because they represent the innovation team's dreams. The problem is that every zombie project slowly bleeds off both manpower and money, thereby diverting resources from the development of new projects with more potential.

Zombies abound in the innovation space. I am reminded of the dancing robots that IBM used to send to major events. The robots were designed to have basic, scripted conversations with an IBM employee and when asked, could dance. They were always crowd pleasers and gave everyone a laugh, though in the end I doubt they did anything to foster sales. What the audience never saw, however, was the preparation required to make these robots work. They were flown in a week beforehand and lab teams had to prepare them many days in advance. Staffers had to memorize the scripts, ensure the robots were appropriately updated and practice to make sure the robot understood the presenter's voice. Just to make sure that it would all work perfectly, two robots were prepared in case one had a glitch. In the end, many days of labor were required by lab staff for the robot's 10-minute performance. In their own way the robots were zombies, consuming precious resources that should have gone to more productive activities.

One of the better ways that projects fall behind at labs is attributable to collaboration with the business for which they are building. I say "better" because it ensures that the lab is collaborating with the business, and any delays are shared mutually. Typical delays in this scenario result from waiting for funding after the project is sold to management, or getting the business unit to focus and commit to its objectives for the build. These are significant issues, but they are readily manageable, especially compared to deal-stoppers like an unforeseen technology failure.

I've made the case that innovation projects don't conform to most norms of project management. There are, however, a number of standards that good innovation project managers do abide by. The best ones always respond meaningfully to staffers' requests for feedback or other information. These managers reach out and seek help when they need it, and are consummate experts at figuring out how to prioritize work in progress. They deliver on their promises to keep senior management and business unit managers abreast of developments. They don't shy away from admitting when things are going badly. Just because innovation projects are different doesn't mean that staff assigned to a project get a pass from normal standards of communication for your organization. In fact, the need for regular communication, both among project team members and in their collaborations with other units, is higher with innovation than with any other group. In addition, there are myriad decisions that need to be made on the fly, any one of which may need to be retracted or revised. Regardless of whether the project achieves its goals, at the end of the project the best innovation project managers celebrate or honor their team's efforts.

FLIP YOUR HACKATHON

Hackathons and other competitions—in which you bring in young people to have a go at innovating for you—are yesterday's solution to developing innovation and exposing your company to new tech. If you want to bring innovation to your company, run hackathons internally in order to invest your time and effort bettering your own workers' skills.

All the same, hackathons are still a hot topic. It's worth explaining why these programs fail both young people and the companies that sponsor them. When the concept was created in the late 90's, it served a real purpose. It gave both young people and tech start-ups an access point into companies that had not yet formalized a process for introducing digital innovation into their operations. Hackers provided fresh insights, and companies got to preview new technology and talent.

Now things have moved on considerably. The process for introducing new ideas and new tech has been formalized with the creation of in-house innovation labs. This means hosting an external hackathon has become redundant. If your lab team is doing their job, you shouldn't be seeing anything proposed externally that your lab team hasn't already suggested or at least mentioned. This is their job: to spot where new technology and innovations can help. While students and start-ups can bring new perspective to solving a problem, a hackathon is almost certainly not the best platform for extracting it. Hiring a few more student interns, or better yet commissioning a POC with a start-up, will do more.

Another factor against them is that hackathons have been generally abused by the corporate promoters as marketing events. In return for sponsoring the event, the company gets good press, showing them engaging in community service and conspicuously promoting innovation within their company. Both claims are far from reality. A typical hackathon actually reaches a tiny percentage of a university's students or the start-up community. As for the students, a more traditional, corporate-sponsored outreach program—in which executives mentor or lecture university students over a prolonged engagement—would certainly reach more young people and provide greater learning opportunities than a hackathon. As for the start-ups, an evaluation process that leads to a real funded POC would be preferred by virtually every start-up owner. On the final point of promoting innovation internally, it's hard to see how spotlighting outsiders' innovation accomplishments and throwing a party afterwards will boost morale and initiative among your staff. All companies need to learn how to innovate for themselves, not pay others to do it for them.

© marketoonist.com

I've spoken with several winners of hackathons, which revealed an interesting pattern of corporate behavior. More often than not, the end results were lackluster both for the winning team and the institution. Without a real plan to integrate the technology, or willingness to pay the winning team to build a version that would actually work, you aren't going to get much utility out of the experience. Even more problematic is the staged nature of these events: in most cases the challenges posed to hackers fell short of real-world conditions. They were designed to be solvable given the time constraints and the students' lack of business experience. Contrast this with the tough situations your lab will confront, characterized by more nuanced or complex problems and no right or wrong solutions, which demand their best effort performed under time and budget constraints.

What typically happens after an external hackathon? At larger corporate events, the winners are brought into the company and encouraged to show off their work to executive teams. If funds are available, and this is always in doubt, the team then settles into trying to build the solution in a way that is meaningful to corporate. And here's what they learn along the way: the IT department's restrictions may demand a near-complete rethink of the system, various departments will fight over the product's feature set, and in the worst case, compliance or other security issues act to prohibit the innovation from ever being deployed. All of which the team is incapable of resolving as they are not players in the company's politics or power structure; they can't change a culture they're not part of.

To paraphrase the assessment of several hackathon winners, "We had to show everyone in the bank how our system worked, we explained it dozens of times to people in multiple departments. In the end we gave away all of our IP and got nothing in return. They wouldn't buy our systems because of compliance issues but we still had to teach them everything we know." This outcome is common. In a hackathon I ran, I witnessed business leaders praise the winners as near-geniuses, saying their solution would revolutionize their business. Several weeks later I was surprised to discover that there was no budget to hire the students as interns over winter break, to build the solution. There was no follow-through, and no adoption of the new technology.

Internal hackathons for your employees, in which the innovation lab staffers team up with individuals from other departments, is a very different story. This is a fantastic way to bring fresh thinking to your business units and make them feel part of the innovation process. The focused nature of the event helps break employees out of their work mindset and gives them a swift, hard reset. They have the opportunity of working in teams, and even have a bit of competition to spur activity. It's a great process.

> *"Innovations developed at employee-sponsored hackathons will be based on real business conditions."*

At the same time, the innovation lab benefits from contact with the business units and the "quality time" they have together to solve real problems. It will energize your business staff and give them hands-on experience innovating. In addition, those outside the innovation lab get exposure to technology they would not have access to in their normal work. It is a winning proposition for both the innovation lab throwing the event and the business unit promoting the event to its staff, since both gain a better appreciation of each other's work.

What's more, any innovations developed at employee-sponsored hackathons will be based on real business conditions and therefore have a higher chance of being implemented than those from student events. Your staff understands the business, all of its rules, and has a more acute perspective on what processes need to be digitized to make them more efficient. That's why the time they spend at an employee hackathon is so valuable. You are mining your corporate IP and getting tremendous insight into your business from people who both know and care.

Of course there is no indicator light or warning sign that flashes and says you need to hold an employee hackathon; the timing is up to you. If you're serious about innovation, and have outdated processes that need revision and digitization, you're ready to go. The impact to your company's culture will be significant and show that innovation is more than just the latest corporate buzzword.

Holding the event itself isn't hard. The difficulty comes afterwards, when the winning proposers have to collaborate with your lab team to build the solution. This may take time, and result in winning team members being posted to the lab for a substantial period. It also takes resources. Hosting a hackathon but then not building or prototyping a new system would be disastrous, since given the initial ballyhoo everyone will be waiting to see the results.

To sum up, hosting a typical outward-facing hackathon will not make your company one bit more innovative. Student or start-up hackathons are still popular, but the best way to view celebrating outsiders' accomplishments with a big event is the same as a party for a winning sports team: the festivity is only a temporary alliance; it does not make us athletes or innovators ourselves. The stakes are high in the innovation business; it needs to be a participatory sport and your team needs to train hard to prepare your company for the future. Hackathons that bring together your innovation lab and your business staff are an entirely different thing. This creates a culture that makes your employees part of the innovation process rather than the victims of innovation's changes.

TRANSFORM, NOT DISRUPT

It's just a word—and I can understand why readers wonder why I would make a fuss about it. The answer is, words matter. How they are used within your organization's innovation program is important both to the lab and to the message sent to the rest of your company. Any employee hoping to "disrupt" their own operation has to be ready for commensurate consequences from your existing operation and staff. If this is the message you intend, great—in extreme circumstances blowing it up may be the best (and possibly the only) strategy. If not, it's reasonable to assume that you are instead attempting to "transform"—a more positive, less threatening, set of actions.

To make the point crystal clear, let's look at the two definitions:

disrupt

1. interrupt (an event, activity, or process) by causing a disturbance or problem.

   throw into confusion, throw into disorder, throw into disarray, cause confusion/turmoil in, play havoc with, derange, turn upside-down, make a mess of; disturb, disorder, disorganize, disarrange

transform

2. make a marked change in the form, nature, or appearance of.

change, alter, modify, convert, metamorphose, transfigure, transmute, mutate; remodel, reshape, remould, redo, reconstruct, rebuild, recast, reorganize, rearrange, reorder, reshuffle, restyle, rejig, rework, renew, revamp, renovate, overhaul, remake, revolutionize, stir up, turn upside-down

From those definitions you can see that the message of transformation is just as powerful as disruption, and, if you think about it, more appropriate for your business. Would you rather "interrupt by causing a disturbance or problem" or make a "marked change in form, nature, or appearance of" your business? The latter is more appropriate for most and does not in any way signify that the measures are half-hearted or less effective. The end results are the same, but the messaging, especially within your company, is very different.

Tell your lab to go out and disrupt your company and see what happens. You are encouraging direct conflict between your existing employees and your laboratory. Lab staff will tell your business units that they are coming to bring "disruption" and that they should be willing participants when they are asked to pitch in and help. The immediate response from your staff will be, "What have we been doing so wrong that we need to be disrupted?" and "How can I maximize my chances of surviving this disruption?" It is highly unlikely that they'll give their wholehearted support to the lab, and even less likely that they'll be vested in and cheering any project that the lab proposes.

Setting a lab the unfettered goal of disruption is particularly problematic given the youthful nature of the perpetrators. It is perfectly natural for young people to want to change everything.

For them, the processes that are currently in place seem antiquated. They, being young and inexperienced, feel that disrupting the old ways via tech is both natural and correct. Eager to earn their keep, they'll have no problem sowing seeds of upheaval within your organization, and some will do it with glee.

Staff in the business units do not share the mantra of disruption. They've been hard at work on whatever task they've been asked to complete. While going digital may be on their minds, being disrupted, and possibly made redundant by digital, is not high on their list of priorities. For them disruption is a trigger word. Once unleashed it will doubtless cause apprehension. These are people who, through years of labor and loyalty, have earned the right to be a participant in the changes coming to their workplace. It is their IP that you want to retain and improve through digitization. Most will be willing to help "transform" their workplace to make their work easier, better or more interesting. Many (though clearly not all), will be happy to help and have no shortage of ideas if you take the time to ask, examine their work flows, and include them in the solution.

Transformation is much less threatening a goal to your staff, and a better basis upon which labs can start their new relationship with the business units. It brings a message that the employees' jobs have value, and implies a level of inclusion in the changes that will occur during transformation. The employees have earned it. More importantly, a lab can't disrupt or transform on its own. Recall that your lab isn't the master of any process within your business, and has to draw IP from business units in order to change anything. This is why the talk of disruption rings hollow for many young innovators. They may hold the keys to the digital kingdom, but exactly what are they going to digitize? This entire process of transformation is easier and more productive if done in collaboration with staff that feel included and respected.

Why are so many labs talking about disruption? For one, it's instinctual for these folks to obsess about big ideas that change everything. It's what they're paid to do (from the macro perspective) but they're confusing something here. Disrupting the competition is fantastic, but disrupting their parent company is harmful over the short and possibly the long term as well. This problem also plagues upper management—they haven't been thinking clearly about what disruption means for their existing employees, and how digital initiatives will graft into their company. It sounds great, until they have to clean up the mess left behind by infighting, disruptions gone bad, and even internally sabotaged innovation projects.

A great example of how to transform properly can be seen in the Singaporean bank OCBC. As of this book's printing, OCBC has put together a new training facility designed to up-skill and re-skill employees as part of their "digital transformation program." There it is front and center, the word transformation. The central tenet of the program is "No one is left behind." This dramatically eases employee fears of being made redundant. Employees use the new facility to become skilled with digital technologies and map out a course for their future at the bank. Here's what makes the program special: every employee has been put on notice that business as usual is over. Everyone is aware of the bank's intent to go digital, that they need to contribute, and that the bank's look and actions will change significantly in the coming two to five years. Despite the speed and depth of the transformation, the bank is messaging that it will be done in collaboration with employees. Clearly both management and employees are aware that job changes and job losses are coming, but at least employees have a fighting chance to participate. Their innovation lab is fundamental to this program. Seeds are being sown for better integration of lab and business employees. This is happening via "transformation" not "disruption."

If you've already been sending your employees word of coming disruption, perhaps it's time to pull back and reconfigure a few of your strategic goals. To quell the understandable fears, your message should be one of inclusion and collaboration, emphasizing that these values have a role to play. Urging participation in digital projects is vital. Immediately change your lab's rhetoric to be employee-sensitive. Damage already done will not be repaired immediately, but the path ahead will become less confrontational. Naturally, "disruptive projects" that are already underway need revisiting. Fears of isolation and neglect, if held by members of a business unit, must be first understood and then critically addressed. Undoubtedly, digital projects will cost jobs. If migration paths for these employees haven't been discussed, then it's time to pause and have these talks, as challenging as they may be. Here, the lab can help only to the extent that they predict what the future staffing needs will be. They only bring about the transformation. Reorganisation post-digital adoption is rightly the responsibility— and obligation—of competent upper management.

78% of innovation portfolios are allocated to continuous innovation instead of disruptive risks.
CB Insights, "State of Innovation" Survey of 677 Corporate Strategy Executives

The message of disruption is a powerful one. It should be used with utmost caution internally, even when painted as an external bogeyman threatening an entire industry sector that does not "go digital." Indeed, the motivation for most companies to start a lab in the first place is fear of being disrupted themselves. Something interesting is going on here: there's a widespread misperception that all companies will be "Amazon'd" or "Uber'd" out of existence by some giant threat. In some industries these fears are rational but for the majority they are not. Change will occur much more subtly than that. More commonplace is the slow, invisible disruption being played out with data and back office systems, whose changes are imperceptible to the naked eye. These are reconfiguring the very heart of internal systems, and it has a shocking impact on employees. Disruption is an obvious threat from without, and an insidious, stealthy one from within. Thus, using this term as a motivational tool or rallying cry is fraught with peril; the implications are too well understood by employees already uncertain about their future. Allowing an innovation lab to trumpet this term unthinkingly is like allowing kids to play with dynamite.

Do not let your labs fixate on disruption as the end goal of their labour, because it isn't. Often a lab's fixation on disruption is innocently driven by the digital culture that your lab staff admires and emulates, even if it may not be wholly appropriate to your organization. Letting the message spread and fester may do more harm than good for the morale in your company. Transformation as a mantra is more appropriate because it is implicitly inclusive within your business units, and creates an environment where employees are more likely to feel vested in the process. Disruption is among us and no one denies that there are business models that are being upended. In these cases, disruption should be addressed by senior management with sensitivity, resolve, and strategic planning, while the innovation lab gets on with tech solutions to underpin them.

11

THE CINO VS THE CIO

Fair warning: this chapter also has its explosive elements. It may offend (unintentionally) many from both the CIO and CTO camps—i.e., those who hold these titles as well as team members who report to them. I offer my apologies in advance. I've got no innate grudge against either group. As a long-term innovator, however, I've been locked in mortal combat with both and so I understand comprehensively how difficult it is to innovate given fixed systems, fixed mindsets, and preconceptions about the way things are done. The fundamental issue is these two groups are the standard-bearers for the systems and processes that are currently in place. This tends to make them resistant to the ones your company will need in the future.

In this book I am guilty of blurring the distinctions between a CIO and CTO. Why? The key point is not their differences but what they have in common: broadly speaking, neither one is properly suited to running an innovation program. This is not due to incompetence: both positions are critical to running your existing computer systems, which are the backbone of your current success. That said, in most cases they will not be the key element of your digital transformation. Neither these executives nor their teams are disposed to developing the next-generation skills needed to move your business forward. More importantly, writing off innovation and the very future of your company as one more IT project, undertaken by the usual IT people, is not a strategy to bank on.

Why do I hold this view? Neither of these roles has had, as a standard remit, bridging tech and the business units to build product, though one could argue that CTOs do this to a limited extent. If your innovation program changes one and only one thing within your company, it should be to involve business unit leaders at the onset of new digital projects. This is a sea change from the past, where business leaders told the IT department what they needed, and were somewhat passive participants in its implementation. Thanks to the client-centric style of digital development that innovation labs and programs are adopting, that's no longer the case. The people who know your clients best are your front-line business owners. Their participation in building and designing new systems separates "digital transformation" from what your IT department does, which is buying and running new software.

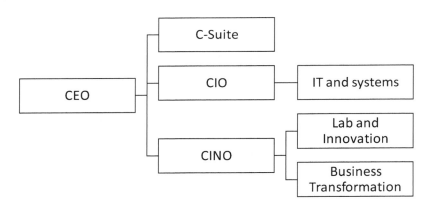

The Chief Innovation Officer (CINO) gets a seat on the C-suite to better promote innovation, and for access to the CEO in cases where conflict resolution is necessary.

I celebrate the efforts of your CIO and CTO; I do not intend to belittle their contributions. The problem is that their strength rests in keeping your systems going. They tend to deal with known quantities and fairly strict parameters. Expecting an IT team to assess how AI technology can be used to modify a business process and transform your business is unrealistic. These specifications were simply not in their job descriptions and are not part of the culture of the department they serve. What these people do is define the environment and technology upon which your systems will run, and keep it running to specification. This is mission critical and an integral part of your transformation strategy. But it's not the same thing as developing a new user interface or reimagining a business process.

The creation of an independent Chief Innovation Officer (CINO) is mandated because innovation's challenges go above and beyond systems design. While there are CIOs and CTOs who can make the transition (I know of some who have done so with distinction), there needs to be an independent point person to resolve the special sorts of problems that will manifest as you innovate. Given their profile, expecting a CIO/CTO to overhaul years of "best practice" in order to introduce an innovative product is not a natural ask. Your innovation lab will be far better off having someone with clout situated squarely in their camp, to advocate their needs and proposals. This is why Kelly Johnson's first rule for his skunk works was that the team's head report to a division president. He could perceive the problem firsthand: innovation encroaches on so many different mangers' territories that the only way to get resolution is a direct report to the top. Digital transformation challenges preconceived notions on how to run systems, and poses hard questions about what levels of change or risk are acceptable. Such policy decisions need sponsors from within to help them get attention, gain traction, and generate decisions from top management. The formation of a CINO position converts an innovation lab from a feel-good proposition to a real agent for change.

Let me use a real-life example to demonstrate how conflicts arise that can cause real damage. In this major financial service company, innovation came hard. The offices were old and dingy, and frankly so was the management team, who were as digitally resistant as they come. They administered a tried-but-true product portfolio that was considered a gold mine, but was starting to show its age. For some years, they placed innovation under the CIO's portfolio because it was expedient. Now, the CIO was fantastic at this job, miraculously keeping obsolete legacy systems running on a shoestring budget for years, demonstrating resourcefulness and dedication.

Here's the problem: Innovation resources fell within the same budget as the CIO's systems budget. This meant that any pennies sent to innovation came from the already skimpy pot for systems upkeep and maintenance. Of course the CIO underfunded innovation—he was determined to focus time and resources toward keeping their aging systems up and running. Innovation was a backwater and suffered because of it. Stresses grew as their successes were few and far between. The problem came to a climax and the decision was taken to create a separately funded CINO position that extracted both personnel and resources from the CIO. This created intense conflict. An honorable and otherwise superb CIO was left disgruntled by the sudden removal of these responsibilities. Wouldn't it have been easier if this had been done from the start? A valuable employee was left seething, innovation was delayed, and a toxic environment left to fester—all because no one initially saw a difference between these equally critical roles.

Besides advocacy, the other critical function of the CINO is to keep the parallel requirements of "two speed" development and architecture on track. This model posits that within a corporation, there are two distinctively different development modes and often two separate systems running them. This is strategic, for segregating development into fast and slow modes frees up two different mindsets, beliefs and behaviors for building optimizing systems.

In fast development, the goal is to get new innovations up and running as quickly as possible to aid in transforming the business. Similarly, new digital offerings or "systems of engagement" are rolled out to clients as quickly and easily as possible. Typically, and ideally, an innovation lab works in fast development mode. They use "agile development" protocols to build new software and get new technology up and running as quickly as possible. Usually the projects are built on cloud systems, which provide a flexible and fast development environment that also serves to segregate the projects from existing systems. The developers' mindset is to work as a team, making iterations with each pass, improving the product while maintaining flexibility to changes. These teams want to build a viable product as expeditiously as possible; if that means leaving a feature off the product for now, so be it, since time to marketplace is critical.

Slow development takes place on what are commonly referred to as a business's "core systems." These are the databases and other underlying software that have powered the business for years and provide the "systems of record." They are frequently run on mainframes or large on-site servers and do an admirable job of keeping the business going. They tend to be inflexible and are not designed for change. Any alterations to core systems come at a slow pace. This is appropriate, as mistakes can cause service disruptions or data loss. Getting it wrong on core systems can be expensive. So, core systems are treated with care, and changes are monitored with caution. This entails the use of "waterfall" methodologies, in which each stage of development is completed to near perfection before the next phase is initiated. The result is that everything is built only once, to a high-quality standard. While your lab will work *with* core systems, they generally avoid working *on* them because they are so sensitive to change. Most innovators take the data or calculations from core systems and repurpose them, while leaving the systems untouched.

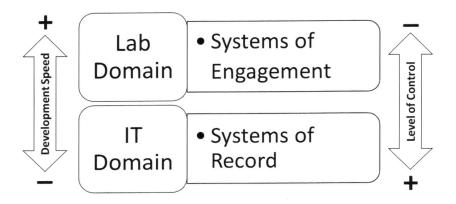

Two-speed development ensures that client-facing systems of engagement are updated more frequently by the lab, using a more nimble control. Systems of record or core systems change slowly to ensure they are rock solid and are in the hands of the IT department with heavy control.

Debates are ongoing in the management consulting community over the success and the sustainability of two-speed development. The parallel approach can be complicated and, in the end, frustrating due to the conflicting differences in expectations. It is a real problem, yet I think it will ease as core systems modernize and as agile-style development becomes the norm. In the meantime, there is no argument that innovation lab initiatives demand a faster development cycle than those relating to core systems. For the moment, two-speed development is the only way forward. Moreover, the turnover for prototyping and delivering lab products is significantly faster than the IT department's standard. Your CIO, who oversees a slower and far more conservative set of operating conditions, may feel discomfort in rolling out a new client-facing portal at the breakneck speed of three months. It's simply not what they do.

This is why I argue that your innovation lab must have a CINO who works outside of the CIO/CTO function. This is in no way to slight the accomplishments of CIOs and CTOs, who tend to provide fantastic service in developing a system's architecture and keeping the systems going. At the same time, CIO/CTOs are typically not the ideal candidates to run an innovation program.

The creation of a Chief Innovation Officer accomplishes two things. First, it establishes oversight for rapid-fire IT development. Second, it gives innovators a seat at the table for conflict resolution and approvals by senior management. In sum, the CINO develops new tech that is responsive to business needs, built in a fast, agile environment. The CIO/CTO develops steadfast and durable core systems. Keeping these roles separate, and understanding their distinctions, is essential to a forward-thinking senior management team.

AVOID INFLATED EXPECTATIONS

You've paid for a new office space that sets the stage for creativity, recruited a team of bright young stars, and expect innovation to start flowing on schedule, much like the crafted coffees they favor. But the big results aren't coming in. What's wrong?

Keeping expectations in line for what your innovation lab can realistically achieve is critical for everyone. Most importantly, do not overestimate what the team can do on its own. All too often the burden of innovation is improperly placed exclusively on the lab when in fact it is a cooperative effort. In order for new innovations to take root, they need sponsors from outside the lab: business units, senior management, compliance and many other actors, who all have a stake in seeing innovation succeed. Without the support of all of these teams, the lab will be hobbled.

Even more detrimental is the widely held belief that the lab will assess your business and dictate suitable innovation while the rest of your organization simply sits back and waits. Nothing could be further from the truth. The young hackers, programmers and 'digirati' who populate innovation labs are not business experts. The fact is they will be blissfully unaware that one of your competitors has launched a new system that lends a competitive advantage. It's not on their radar, and even if it does register, its significance may pass them by, because the business implications—again, not their purview—will escape them. Meanwhile, your business leaders will hear about the same system in a heartbeat, know whether it's making money in a week, and be hell-bent on copying it within a month if they think it's hurting their business. Innovation is a two-way street. It's up to your business units to feed the innovation lab with updates on exactly what is changing in your business. If left to their own devices, labs have neither the product-level expertise nor the bandwidth to track what new tech has hit the market and is changing your domain. It's not their fault. They were hired because they are digital experts, not business experts.

© marketoonist.com

This is precisely why in Chapter 12 ("Build or Buy") I state that your innovation lab should be urged to become the greatest implementers of technology in your company. Ideally there is an ongoing, active feedback loop in place, with business managers who first spot and then call for replication of any significant innovation detected in the market. I am advocating this because the ultimate goal is to beat the competition, which is enabled and trialed by the intermediary step of duplicating tech. The lab must be proficient at that, otherwise you'll be playing a very long game of catch-up. This collaborative effort is also beneficial because it will train your lab to produce results faster, and may provide clarity as to how to surpass competitors' efforts.

This process is key for your lab to master:

- understanding business unit requirements
- reaching out to vendors
- finding the best solution
- negotiating a price for a trial
- assessing its suitability

That depicts a solid innovation lab at work. Otherwise you're still at square one with nice but off-the-mark demos and an attitude of "wouldn't it be nice to try this here."

Sadly, the majority of labs I've worked with do not replicate and improve on competitors' initiatives. Instead, they live in the world of the perpetual zombie demo. Why? Business managers have not been incentivized to work with the labs in their key performance indicators (KPIs). It's interesting that the same senior management that splurges on a new innovation lab fails to impress upon their business leaders that the lab is a tool for competitive advantage, much less a tool for developing innovation themselves. I've seen this missed connection again and again, and it never fails to leave me shaking my head.

A case in point: IBM's lab in Singapore was expensive and it showed, perched on a high floor in the city's financial district with a stunning view of Marina Bay and the Straights—one of the largest and most impressive innovation spaces in all of Singapore. The lab garnered praise from business leaders across the company, as a centerpiece for IBM's clients. The lab's success was tied to IBM's sales force that was in charge of promoting IBM products and the lab to their clients. The lab was not a marketing organization unto itself, instead relying on the sales team to bring in new customers

Since the key means of bringing clients to the lab was the sales force, this would obviously (or so you'd think) mean rewarding the matchmaking in the sales force's incentive agreements. Unfortunately, the sales teams and their managers had no clear incentives or KPIs to work with the lab. They weren't credited in any meaningful way for bringing clients in, and in fact many were not sure that it was a good idea. It became clear, as I spoke with more and more salespeople, that some were biased against it. They felt that their sale could be derailed if a client started poking around the lab and became interested in alternative IBM technology that would not provide them a sales incentive. Teams like my own, which built POCs with new AI tech, were held in even lower regard because we required both time and compensation. In the end, the lack of KPIs or incentives to use the lab dissuaded the salesforce, throttled client interaction, and caused the lab to underperform.

> *"There is a collection of business leaders in every company who are resistant to innovation and wish it would simply go away."*

I will venture that there are occasions when labs fall short of expectations because managers actively ignore them. In virtually every company there is a collection of business leaders who are resistant to innovation and wish it would simply go away. Their stance seems to be: let's postpone innovation for a few more years, or until my retirement, or until a new posting comes my way. I apologize if this comes across harshly, but in my experience, assuming that innovation and your lab will be met with universal approval is unrealistic at best. Lab managers have told me time and again that they're not working on a certain project, or with certain departments, because of managers who are completely resistant, even if the lab has an innovation ready to go. This is another case in favor of KPIs that include an innovation component. Unless the more conservative business managers are gently incentivized, innovation will not take place under their watch. Sadly, the failure is often wrongly ascribed to the laboratory.

Another dark scenario that contributes to inflated expectations is when funding is misdirected and labs can't afford to implement solutions. Budgets are burned through in flashy office space and pricey staff, with too little left over for the actual projects. While it may be reasonable to assume that the lab should win some funding from the business units or executive committee, it's shocking (and shockingly common) to see labs with absolutely no budget to run projects independently. In the end, it's far preferable to run bare-bones offices with ample funding to actually build and buy innovation from the open marketplace. To reiterate, the idea that your innovation team should build all its own tech, without paying for outside assistance, is a gross misunderstanding of their utility and role. They may be underperforming precisely because they can't afford ready-made tech or the expertise required to plug it in at your company.

On this latter point, expertise in running new tech is everything. There are so many new technologies out there that it is impossible for your lab team to know, de facto, how to run all of them. Being able to use consultants efficiently and cost-effectively when necessary is critical in determining exactly how a technology can solve a particular problem, and in pushing projects through to completion.

There is a final, more subtle and sinister problem underpinning lackluster innovation by your lab, one that is so insidious it often goes unnoticed. Your IT and compliance departments may be torpedoing innovation. Why? These stakeholders, who usually hold a blocking vote for innovation, may directly vote against it or more subtly impose conditions that prevent innovation from taking root. Why? Because reassessment of process and procedure in systems or compliance is usually a byproduct of innovation, one or both of these departments may not be open to change and may block innovation in order to maintain status quo. This is why I advocate a new position of CINO, separate from the CIO/CTO chain of command.

I ran into this headlong with one of my clients. They wanted to run one of the newer analytics systems that make exploring data so easy that anyone can do it. So effectively does the analytic systems'

AI enable analytics expertise in non-experts, the users are called "citizen data scientists." I use them myself, and can attest that they give your staff a window into their business that far surpasses what is possible in an Excel-driven world. Imagine my surprise when a bank's innovation lab manager told me that they were allowed to deploy only a single copy of this breakthrough software on a single machine in their lab, due to IT and compliance policies. Meanwhile another of my banking clients was running this software throughout their organization. So my question is, who really runs innovation at your company?

So far, I've picked on sources other than the lab itself for poor innovation performance. Clearly, labs may also share in the blame. There are a number of internal problems that prohibit innovation from turning on like a faucet, despite how much money you spend on it. One that is critical, especially during the start-up process, is the need for innovation team members to learn each other's competencies. Early on, no one knows what technical strengths and weaknesses individuals hold, and therefore who should be assigned what job. It's likely that the better part of a year is required as a settling-in period.

In my own experience, it took more than six months to optimise which team members should handle presenting to clients, which to ideate solutions, and which to interface design. Trial and error led us to become more cohesive as a team and got us there in the end, but it certainly didn't happen overnight. Your python coder may give spectacular client presentations, your data scientists may be project managers in disguise. Hidden skills only emerge when you start to work together and sync as a team. While this was one of the most rewarding aspects of my work, there were more than a few bumps in the road.

It's entirely possible that your lab may not be failing or under-producing; rather, its successes are merely flying below the radar. In the early days, much of the work will be setting the stage on which the lab will build or launch innovation. A significant aspect of the ground-laying will be interfacing with IT and compliance to work out both a standardized build platform and rules that all parties can live with. This will take time, yet (hopefully) won't be prolonged by ill will. The other preliminary task is building demos that show the rest of the company that innovation is coming. They won't be earthshattering, more of a series of "heads up" announcements for a new working mode. Indeed, it's the accumulation of small wins that brings a successful digital transformation to fruition.

PART III

Why Do Labs Fail?

If you like this book and it helps you in some small way, please leave a review on Amazon. Reviews, even short ones, help others cut through the noise and hype surrounding innovation to "recognize the pattern."

PATTERN RECOGNITION

Patterns abound in life, as well as in labs that are failing. My in-depth scrutiny of around 40 labs revealed similarities that typified deeper issues. In failing labs, some combination of the 12 best practices I endorse had been flouted consistently, and dysfunction became embedded in the culture. What was interesting was how frequently the same raft of problems arose at labs that are otherwise distinct in industry, size or mission. The consistency indicates that if labs behave in certain ways, they will falter or otherwise grow increasingly toxic.

I mentioned earlier that the 12 best practices I've laid out are prescriptive—intended to treat symptoms of an illness or disease that don't necessarily all manifest at once. They are therapeutic remedies that you can apply within your lab to encourage improvement. For many labs that are merely underperforming, these fixes should be sufficient to make things better. My bet is that improvements will be easy to discern and the mere exercise of reviewing and revising the relationship with your lab or your parent will make all stakeholders happier. All parties in the lab relationship recognize that the innovation business is new and in need of constant improvement. Only time will tell if these fixes are enough; displaying evidence of change will lend confidence to everyone that you're on the right path.

Then there are the more serious situations. Some labs are failing badly, either in the eyes of lab staff or the management team. Often there is conflicting opinion on how dire the situation is. While high staff turnover is a clear indicator that something is wrong, it's not always that obvious when things are awry. The lab or its managers may be blind, even to serious problems. Due to my bias as a former lab manager, my view is that management is more apt to treat the lab as an afterthought, wanting to assume that everything is just fine (while their lab staff stew). A few simple tweaks will not fix a lab in such a bad state of disrepair. Stronger solutions are required. It is only by recognizing the symptomatic patterns that we can step in for a major intervention.

Again and again I've seen patterns of misbehavior in troubled innovation labs. I will analyze these patterns using a tried-and-true medical model, employing what doctors refer to as "constellations of symptoms." Discerning these constellations is what allows doctors to diagnosis and cure specific illnesses. It's the same with labs (if you've looked at enough of them and know how to read the signs).

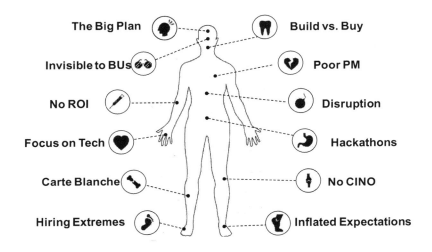

Common symptoms of sickness found in innovation labs. Symptoms result from veering away from best practices. Constellations of symptoms help us diagnose and cure.

The diagram above shows the major indices of sickness for innovation labs; these will form our "constellation of symptoms." They are the inverse of the 12 best practices that I've promoted throughout this book. That is, they are disorders that result when best practices are ignored and things run amok. It is from these 12 symptoms that we will develop the constellations that typify the three most prevalent innovation lab syndromes. Treating symptoms patches the problems, while treating syndromes offers a cure.

INNOVATION THEATER

The first chronic syndrome for innovation labs is something insiders commonly call "innovation theater"—where companies make a big show out of innovating while being far less effective at producing results. These companies tend to get headlines for a series of breathtaking innovations that make competitors green with envy. They may even have a spokesperson for innovation to make it clear they are at the fore. Or so it seems. Closer examination may reveal that innovation is only skin deep, with little actual headway in implementing the solutions that are flowing out of their innovation ecosystem.

There can be no greater example of corporate sponsored innovation theater than the now infamous Silicon Valley tech company Theranos. Based on innovation hype alone, its market capitalization rose to $US 9 billion with 800 employees at its peak. It was adored by the media, which it used to fuel its valuation. Reports of their prowess in revolutionizing blood testing using "nanotainer" technology and the "Edison" analysis machine were ubiquitous. These helped garner a visit by U.S. Vice President Joe Biden, and cast a spell over usually skeptical investors. If ever there was a champion of pathbreaking that rivaled the late Steve Jobs, it was the charismatic, black-turtleneck-wearing, Stanford drop-out Elizabeth Holmes. When the innovations didn't live up to the hype, the now disgraced CEO simply lied and coerced others into doing the same to cover up their deception.

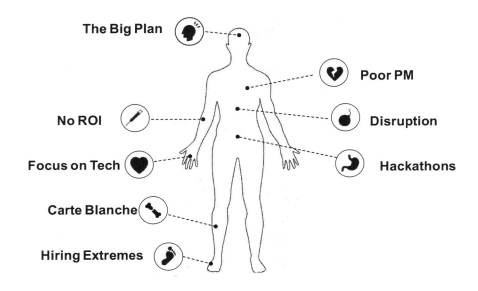

Constellation of symptoms indicative of "innovation theater."

Not only did the company over-report its breakthroughs; it misled investors to the point that the SEC pursued fraud charges against senior officers. Elizabeth Holmes has now been charged with criminal fraud against doctors, patients, and investors. This is subsequent to her reaching a settlement with the SEC, which levied cash penalties, share forfeiture, and a 10-year ban from leadership in publicly owned companies. Other senior corporate officers have been indicted for fraud and still more are fighting SEC charges. The company has been dissolved with $60 million in debts of which an estimated $5 million will be repaid.

This is not to suggest that innovation theater on this scale is something your company would engage in, but it does serve to illustrate how powerful the illusion of "new and better" really is. Innovation has real value, but it can be a potent tool for management to wield to increase the perceived value of the company. This is why many companies inflate their latest achievements, as a demonstration that they are poised for the future. Innovation pays, not just in the tangible new tech, but in terms of the opinion of the outside world. Amplifying the extent of innovative achievement makes analysts, shareholders, and potential investors happy. As a result, innovation theater will always be with us.

The big question is, to what degree? Labs in which theater overrides the creation of workable tech have a characteristic look and feel, and a typical constellation of symptoms. First, they tend to proclaim that their mission is lofty, that it will disrupt the normal operation of the institution, and that the plan is not just big—it's massive! So massive, in fact, that it can be achieved only after several years of diligent work. Of course the cost will be miniscule when compared to the enormous payout. This big plan relies on a critical new technology, whether AI, blockchain or "nanotainers." The technology itself is being sold as a game-changer. Your staff will simply get on board when it launches, so including them in the development stages would just slow down the entire process.

Keeping the company in the press is critical; lab team members are perpetually at conferences pitching their view of the future, which is amplified by corporate PR and senior executives. High visibility hackathons are also favorite ploys because they generate press that keeps the company in the headlines and elevates its reputation for being innovative. Finally, the lab staff is full of energetic young people who are willing to throw themselves diligently at any problem; they have little knowledge of the actual business, but tremendous faith that some senior manager has judiciously surveyed the business landscape. While this may sound suspiciously like Theranos, it could be any innovation lab that seeks to pump up its perceived value within the company or score points with access to the press. This sums up the constellation of symptoms of innovation theater and why, for a multitude of reasons, some labs may be more stage sets than genuine agents of change.

As a disease, innovation theater can be chronic or fatal—it hinges on the relationship between the lab and the corporate parent. It's possible to live as theater for a very long time if the lab is content to devise show pieces that don't actually get implemented. Concurrently, the parent, for whatever reason, may find it easier to live with the façade, while business proceeds as usual. If you think that this devil's bargain is rare, you're mistaken. Many innovation labs fall into this category—some by explicit agreement, others because they are caught in an impasse with their parent. Staffers have a sense of resignation that their products don't get anywhere, but nonetheless believe that they should just keep at it. At the very least, they get to give great tours to visitors. Innovation theater only becomes fatal when the impasse ends, with innovators moving on as they sense that despite their optimism, nothing will ever come of their work.

Overhauling innovation theater is not strictly necessary. If everyone involved is relatively content, and if the publicity is beneficial, by all means keep at it. As cynical as this sounds, there will be some who will be happy to live with this arrangement. In most cases, however, this marriage of convenience isn't stable and it will be up to the lab to make changes to escape from irrelevance. For what it's worth, corporate parents generally are the instigators in creating innovation theater. Their desire for good public relations trumps their desire to implement real change. They create a feedback cycle that rewards the lab for getting in the press and making the company look good. The parent then doubles down by giving the lab latitude to think big, so long as the projects are newsworthy.

In the end, the reward system needs to be changed to bring the lab back into relevance. Their incentive structure needs to be overhauled to reward incremental, documented, implemented innovation. Pay them to get into your company's fabric instead of generating good PR. Typically, the lab must initiate this process and get management on board. This will be difficult as management is likely happy with the status quo. To effect a redirection the lab must first show management the future they are missing out on by not innovating. This is a difficult task that is somewhat akin to shaming executives into true innovation. Ideally, this would be followed by a proposal in which the lab negotiates a position where it can profit or otherwise benefit from any real innovation it develops. A successful proposal means a sea change in the dynamics between the parent and lab. First and foremost, the lab will have a financial interest in the success of its projects, and management may thus be sufficiently vested in the process to accept more innovation. In an earlier chapter I mentioned that ROI was important because it made the lab "players" in the corporate battle for resources. Similarly, the moment the lab can generate profit from an innovation, the lab becomes a player rather than a theater.

It's difficult to demonstrate that "innovation theater" exists, at large companies or their labs, aside from anecdotal accounts from within. Internal accounts are helpful, but need to be carefully weighed since on occasion the stories may be the venting of frustration by thwarted or otherwise aggrieved innovators. The best way to check would be to review the projects that received publicity after a few years, to see if anything came from them. That said, Theranos kept up the ruse for nearly 12 years before reality caught up.

Intriguingly, a recent report from CB Insights titled "JP Morgan Chase Competitive Strategy Teardown: How the Bank Stacks Up On Fintech and Innovation," seems to reveal innovation theater, and on a grand scale. It may be the first (and admittedly tenuous) quantified proof that innovation theater actually exists. The research used artificial intelligence and analyzed the number of times "tech," "technology," and "digital," were referenced in earnings calls during the period 2009-2017 for a number of large (bulge bracket) banks. Earnings calls are important: they are management's primary means of updating shareholders on the company's progress, assuring them of the soundness of their investment, and allowing for "future-looking statements" that reinforce the message of progress.

The results below show Bank of America and Barclays using these terms with the greatest frequency—clear leaders in this regard. The natural assumption would be that these institutions are also leaders in digitization, and, as a corollary, are heavily investing in the future of digital banking as a means of both self-preservation and guaranteeing shareholders' interests.

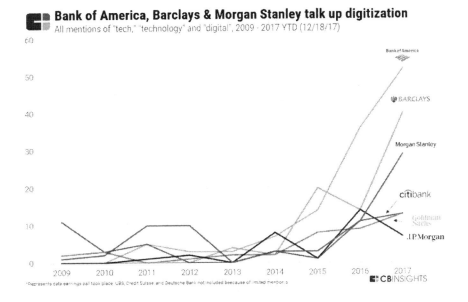

Source: CB Insights

However, the frequency of citing innovation buzzwords may not be a reliable index. CB Insights analysts go on to examine the total investments made in "fintech M&A." This figure is not a surrogate for overall corporate investment in digitization, but it certainly reflects corporate intent within the new digital frontier. Interestingly, the two "winners" in the digital keyword tally rank low on the scale of actual fintech investment. This is a surprising result given the relative emphasis on these terms in investor calls.

Goldman, Citi are the most active bulge bracket banks in fintech investing

Total fintech investments, 2013 - 2017 YTD (12/18/2017)

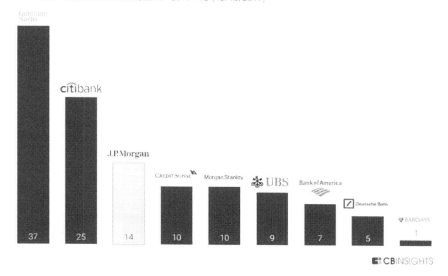

Source: CB Insights

The point, elegantly made by the CB Insights report, is that actual investment in digital and tech does not correlate to the sign-posting of it. This does not mean that innovation isn't happening at these institutions. It clearly is, and what's more, the internal investments in digital mentioned in the report are significant. It does, however, raise the age-old question of whether "talking the talk" is a reliable correlate of "walking the walk."

More to the point, is this disconnect quantitative proof of innovation theater? To be certain, one would need to know the context in which every one of these terms was used during the earnings calls, and map it to a more exacting analysis of overall digital spending. Unfortunately I don't have this data. I do believe that this may be as close as we can get to quantifying the "innovation theater" phenomenon.

MISSION MALPRACTICE

The next constellation of symptoms we'll cover is what I call "mission malpractice." It occurs when an innovation lab lacks focus on two things: what to innovate, and how to do it. These labs are "lost in space" because they don't have a clear trajectory and moreover may be blazing through resources thanks to projects created internally, from the ground up. Add high expectations from the corporate parent to the mix and you've got an absolutely combustible situation.

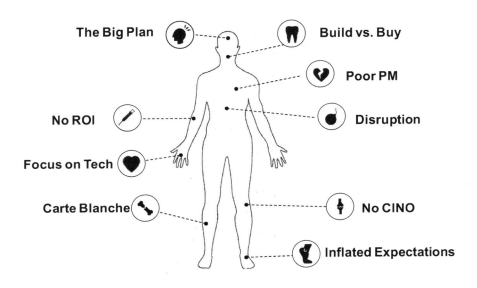

Constellation of symptoms indicative of "mission malpractice."

Interestingly, young teams aren't the only ones that get stuck in this trap. Older, more experienced staff are equally likely to succumb due to the novel parameters of running innovation projects, or overly ambitious promises for delivery. Even if they come from or are in good communication with the business units, and are engaged in active dialogue to find solutions, optimism and inflated ambitions (the big plan) divert them from more modest, guaranteed advances. It's not that they aren't trying, in fact they're giving it 100%. But they're shooting for the moon, when small local gains are a better option.

Here's a cautionary tale. A certain highly effective CEO of a start-up financial services company was hot to innovate. He had an innate love of tech that was praiseworthy, but had no direct experience with building or implementing new solutions himself. Keen to begin, he put everything in place including funding, a stellar team that loved him, technical build teams on call, and of course a penchant for anything new innovative and flashy. His small company was his built-in innovation lab, with everyone starting at ground zero, ready to implement a new digital journey at a moment's notice. The big question was, what would they make?

This CEO had one eye on innovation in the outside world and loved every new digital invention he saw, the more complex the better. He talked to anyone even peripherally involved in the market and brought lots of tech in. He had complete "carte blanche." His team was soon overwhelmed, not just from how much he brought, but from the disparate fields it encompassed. There was no overarching mission to use tech in a scheduled or organized manner. Individual projects got underway, then got sidetracked or interrupted for the latest new fad that caught the CEO's fancy. The result was a vicious cycle of half completed projects, false starts, and conceptual overload for the build teams.

There were additional challenges. The CEO was willing to buy some technology from the marketplace, ordinarily a good thing, but the company was simultaneously undergoing a systems overhaul that complicated any potential implementation. The team knew what systems were currently in place but weren't sure what they would have in a year's time. This created additional stress, because any bought-in tech had to be evaluated for use on both current and ill-defined future platforms. This meant two migration paths and a doubling of the labor for any new technology. It eventually became too much for everyone to bear.

In the end, with so many false starts and moonshot-caliber projects crashing and burning, the investors began to question the CEO's technical management skills. Their solution was to bring in an experienced tech builder who was forcibly placed in the company to set the company's innovation on the right course. The CEO is still there and remains a great asset, but his inability to focus on an achievable mission and disciplined project management cost him. He now defers tech to his colleague and no longer calls the shots in this area.

Mission malpractice is a two-way street. Both the lab and corporate oversight must work together to recognize and fix existing problems. A mission is typically lost because no set of measured expectations exists at the onset. Many labs are so new that managers are reluctant to put them on a production schedule. Fear of too much supervision results in far too little. The remedy is obvious: establish loose expectations as to the number, timing, and types of projects that the lab should try to attain. "Loose" because a lab shouldn't be subject to the same constraints as existing businesses.

Here's why small-scale, measurable gains are so important. You can have a situation where inside the lab everything seems great, the staff are busy with a large project, grinding away every day, building to the max. It's just a matter of time until the mission is a success. But at what opportunity cost? As time and resources are expended on one project, dozens of others are slipping away (with uncalculated ROIs) and innovation is lost. A hardworking team doesn't mean innovation is forthcoming. In fact, if there is a big plan in play, it could mean that innovation isn't happening at all. Poor project management compounds this problem. Agile builds with a small staff suck up their bandwidth. It's hard to keep several going at once, any one of which might be more important to your company. The same problem occurs when labs try to do too much at once and get off-mission by trying to be too many things.

Mission malpractice need not be fatal. If it were a disease, a single dose of strong antibiotics would be prescribed. The solution for your innovation lab is equally straightforward. Without casting blame, sit down with everyone to understand what tracks the team is on and whether it's working optimally. The points of discussion aren't just the success of a single project, but the number of projects underway, the likelihood they will be implemented, the adoption of documented project management, and a cold hard look at the utility prospects within given timeframes. The lab manager needs to get consensus on expectations, for both the overall mission and the production attainable from his team. Frankly, it may be time to pull the plug on the big-plan project your lab is working on. Redirecting resources to ensure that other projects get built and that the singular focus of the lab shifts is likely to involve some near-term disappointment, but will eventually make everyone happier.

BU BREAKDOWN

There are many innovation labs stuck in a malaise of mediocrity that they can't seem to escape. What is heartbreaking is that so many lab staffers are unfulfilled in their work and often refer to the parent organization as if it were populated by space aliens. The people doing the complaining are among the most highly skilled workers at your firm, and you are building your future upon their commitment. They are working in your highest profile venture and while they may not be universally miserable, many are less happy than they ought to be, considering the freedom they've been given to break new ground. The easy and somewhat lazy answer is to blame this on clichéd millennial discontent, but the better course is to take a hard look at the source of their dissatisfaction.

The fact is, their work may be innovative and their mastery of tech impressive, but they are disconnected from on-the-ground applications. It makes a big splash as a demo when you bring guests to the lab, but no one really knows how to use it for real. Of all the maladies that can afflict a lab community, this is doubtless the most sinister and most prevalent. I call it "BU breakdown," which stands for the deterioration in the relationship between the lab and business units. This in turn leads to institutionalized mediocrity in the lab.

"Invisibility" was the first ailment discussed at the onset of this assessment of best practices for innovation labs. Isolation of the lab is the first stage of the breakdown in connectivity to your organization. The second stage is this near-moribund condition—a constellation of symptoms that requires major intervention to effect a cure.

I've seen many examples of this second stage. One in particular comes to mind, at a Singapore laboratory created with high hopes by an insurer. Expense was no object. They splurged on a gleaming innovation space. Rather than go for a modest rental in the industrial park that had been repurposed as an innovation zone, the company opted for a gleaming grade-A office tower—new, beautiful and humming with every convenience. Inside the lab, murals, coffee machines, bean bag chairs and other accoutrements replicated the feeling of working at a Silicon Valley tech giant— which of course, they weren't. The lab was located miles from the main office—and it bore the burden of this isolation. What could possibly go wrong? Put a large team of young people in a beautiful bubble, throw money at them, tell them to innovate, and of course they'll be happy, creative, and productive. Right?

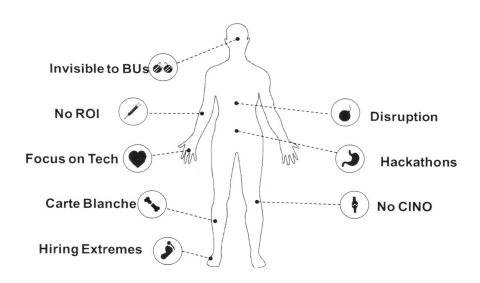

Constellation of symptoms indicative of "BU breakdown."

Four years later, the space still looks great and the free-flow snacks remain a nice perk, but signs of discord are evident. The young techies I met questioned the validity of their work even though everyone seems to love the office space. It's unclear whether innovation is making a return on investment that is satisfactory to management. It's even less clear if the lab is fostering the digitally-minded managers of tomorrow that the business so desperately needs. The firm's competitors are wondering when innovation is going to hit the marketplace and to this end are trying to figure out what, if anything, is going on behind the lab's doors.

To the lab's credit, they are not secretive. They host start-up hackathons where the winners gain cash and employment offers from the parent. It's not a bad program. And not at all a bad idea if you're disconnected from your business units and have to generate innovation in your own bubble. It's far easier to run a competition for others than to buckle down and operate within tight, tedious, real-world business constraints. The benefits of bringing innovation to the company seem tenuous, at best.

As I read about other projects on the company's website, the disconnect is further evident in an HR training tool the lab has produced for internal use. Aside from the likelihood that the cost of developing this tool was greater than buying one from the open market, it's hard to imagine the features being superior to those provided by established software vendors who've been providing digital training for years. But to be fair, let's look at the plus side. After four years, the lab launched a blockchain-based micro-insurance platform that will sift health data from a not-yet-built medical network. This is a great project that ticks the boxes of "blockchain," "big data," and "digital purchase," yet it's hard to see how it pays the rent on the sleek office. More importantly, given that this is the only project in four years that touches the business lines, is this lab living up to its potential?

In direct contrast, we can examine a lab sponsored by a local bank. What makes this facility unique is that business unit personnel work directly with lab personnel to develop banking innovation. The business professionals are seconded to the lab to better understand how both process analysis and innovation can help them. The integration between the BU and the lab is tight, with strong senior management support and new products being launched into the market on a regular basis. It's noteworthy that the young people at this facility speak about their employer with a different vocabulary. Sure, they razz some of their less digitally-inclined colleagues, but

114

overall they feel that they're in this together, and their tone is one of inclusion and collaboration.

Will integrating staff from the BUs and lab effectively guarantee happy young digital geniuses? Probably not, but the innate satisfaction of having a new product, process, or piece of code they've developed at work and contributing to the bottom line goes a long way toward the immediate gratification required by many young people. It ratifies the lab and their sense of self-worth, and they feel a sense of shared responsibility and destiny.

Resolving BU breakdown at your lab will be a challenge; it won't be resolved with a simple sit-down. It requires many joint sessions between the BUs and the lab to find a cure. While this approach should be driven from the top, it can also be generated by the lab staff if they perceive the need for greater inclusion. Most BUs won't initiate this process, as they are locked into their existing mode; unless they're directly threatened by a competitor's new innovation, they'll likely remain disconnected from the lab. In fact, to reduce the hassle factor, some will eschew the lab altogether and seek a third-party tech provider on their own to sell them a solution.

The first step of the cure is to have all parties recognize that the system is broken. The lab being mired in mediocrity and the BUs not getting the innovation they need necessitates a painful culture shift on both sides, involving training and repurposing of people. Of course it won't happen with the flick of a switch. The next step after a cultural reformatting is to initiate joint discussions to pin down exactly where, when, and how innovation should be brought into existing systems. This was what made the aforementioned bank's innovation program so powerful. Rather than a free-floating satellite, the lab was regarded as a valuable resource in which key business figures were routinely immersed in what they saw as the easiest path to implementing innovation.

Initiating work with the innovation team doesn't have to be formal or complicated. Sometimes it's as simple as booking a conference room at the lab's offices and inviting the team to a meeting.

I want to hear from you. The most important "Element of Success" for me is hearing your thoughts on what I write. Reach me through richturrin.com or connect on LinkedIn to join in the discussion: linkedin.com/in/turrin.

PART IV

Elements of Successful Labs

I need your help. As a new author your support is "measurable" in my reviews on Amazon; even a short review helps. My gratitude for you reading this book, your Amazon review, or reaching out to say hello through richturrin.com or LinkedIn is "immeasurable."

MEASURING THE UNMEASURABLE

Imagine an innovation lab that has switched on its latest product enhancement, followed soon thereafter by the company's sales going through the roof. It's a smash hit and everyone is cheering both management and the lab for their foresight and innovation prowess. In an ideal world, your lab could replicate this success and it would be immediate, measurable, and obvious to everyone. In the real world, however, smash hits are hard to come by. This means we have to be creative in how we judge a lab's success.

The goal of this book is to improve exactly that. Yet there's a problem here, one of definition. How do we identify success, and what metrics should we use to measure something as nebulous as innovation? There is no clear answer. No two companies will have the same measurement system, which means a prescriptive solution isn't useful. That's because measuring a lab's contributions largely depends on management's stated aims. These are expressed broadly in the mission statement of the lab, and ideally, more specifically at the start of every new project. Meeting these goals should be the primary metric of success, and its measurement will be, of necessity, an iterative process that is adjusted and improved over the course of the lab operations.

Traditional innovation metrics will not all map with your lab's remit. These include things like the number of patents gained, the budget of the lab relative to sales, and percentage of sales attributable to a new product. Of course, these are solid metrics and I am a strong proponent of estimating ROI for every project. But traditional financial metrics only reveal part of the picture of the state of innovation at your company. Your lab's enterprise goes above and beyond these baseline measures and the less tangible achievements should be acknowledged. This may be at odds with how you evaluate the rest of your business; it's important to remember that the lab is in a unique position to impact your company's future, and much of its work doesn't fit neatly within standard measures. At the very least, granting the lab an exception from traditional metrics is practical, since new labs invariably fail profitability tests during their early years. Counting your lab as a cost center and a drag on revenue as it begins to bring innovation to your company won't make life easier for anyone.

In order to measure lab success effectively we need to look at it from multiple points of view. In this way we can find signs of its good or ill health without relying on any sole number. The basic metrics I suggest are:

1) lab project analytics
2) traditional ROI metrics
3) internal team innovation metrics
4) external collaboration metrics

Taken together, these measures ought to provide a reliable snapshot of the impact the lab has had in your organization. It may do poorly in some while excelling in others. Alternate indices may be valuable for your specific set of circumstances. Creativity is encouraged. To unpack each one in turn, lab project analytics are the most basic measure of your lab's activities and are the simplest place to start. They include: the number of projects, the percentage taken to completion, and the number of useable and unusable outcomes. These are the core statistics the lab lives by; they need to be monitored carefully. That these activities need to be continuously monitored might seem obvious, but, as discussed earlier, there are few fixed norms in managing innovation projects. Keeping a tight watch on these analytics ensures that everyone involved with the lab has a solid grip on how things are going, and what needs attention to pull up to speed.

Things get tricky in qualifying what is a win or a loss. This is where a sit-down at the start of each project is critical. Understanding how the project will be successful and what other potential benefits could come out of it is critical. Many of the project goals and objectives will not be measured in dollar value or completion of some new useable tool. Failure is common in innovation and out of these failures come new ideas.

Imagine a project that fails in its initial goals but proves to be the perfect technology for something else. Has the project failed? Not when you consider that it led to a new path for or application of the technology. This is why discussing what constitutes success or failure is so critical at the outset of the project, along with review at some intermediate state. These sorts of analytics are particularly valuable with projects that elude hard-dollar measures of success. While such success is optimal, it's not always feasible. These analytics bridge that gap by acknowledging and rating projects that do not have a calculable ROI.

ROI is not a realistic measure with every project, but where it fits, it should be brought to bear. Many on the innovation side will chafe at this suggestion. But ROI is no less valid just because it is traditional; it has the added benefit of being used across all of the other business units. The difference with innovation labs is this: the ROI figures are simply part of a broader evaluation scheme. We are not slaves to these numbers; they are only one component of a much bigger picture. With them we can tease out the cost vs revenue generated by individual projects. Of course, a certain flexibility is critical in determining the hard and soft dollars attributable to a project.

Let's look at an example. OCBC Bank in Singapore was the earliest adopter of AI-driven chatbots used in customer service within the local market. Named "Emma," the chatbot was designed to answer some of the most commonly repeated questions about home loans. If a chatbot handled these frequent questions, it would spare everyone in the loan department time and effort. Emma was trained on a limited, specific set of questions, and put to work. After five quarters in operation Emma had answered 100,000 enquiries, facilitated $130M in loans, converted 12% of chats to prospects, and answered 82% of questions correctly. These are impressive metrics, but they do not all immediately convert into hard dollars. This is why understanding and valuing the soft metrics that are intrinsic to an innovation project are so important. Of course, OCBC will not publicly tout the dollar value of Emma's work, but it's clear that the numbers above can be parsed individually and then, with some approximation, converted into an approximate real-dollar value. This is a great example of how soft dollar metrics count every bit as much as hard.

OCBC's Emma has one other lesson to teach us. The bot's sponsor was quick to point out that Emma was built out of the same chatbot technology that powered an earlier, failed lab project. The first try at using the bot failed for a number of reasons, but what is important is that Emma's success came as a direct result of that failure. This raises the tricky question whether the first effort really tanked, or whether it formed part of the experiments that eventually led to Emma's success. This is why failure in innovation is so hard to judge on a binary basis. What the lab learns when applying new technology can make all the difference for the subsequent effort, as it did with Emma.

Internal team innovation metrics capture how the team is doing on the inside, when the doors are closed—how they effect change as a group, how they work together, and whether they can discern conduits that are relevant to your business. They measure internal ideation and ability to coalesce as a team, which is distinct from external collaboration metrics (as important as these are). If the team is going to survive, they need the ability to come together and profit from each other's skills. The very best labs are two-track operations: they collaborate closely and well with the business units, but can also come up with ideas independently. This can only happen with a nurturing and a sustainable home environment. Thus, the internal measures may include new project ideas developed by lab staff, new technologies brought in by the lab, and the enhancement of lab infrastructure via computer networks, demos, and internal training. Attracting and retaining staff is also a critical component since excessive turnover can cause paralysis.

Compare this with external collaboration metrics, which assay how the lab works with the business units and organizations outside of the company. Again, this is a key measure of the lab's overall competence. These departments do not exist as islands; collaboration is exactly why you have opted to install a lab within your company. The lab's ability to create an ecosystem of innovation depends on their ability to reach out to the business units to understand needs and promote innovation. To assess this ability, metrics might include: the number of business units that have active projects, the number of ideas originating on the business side, the number of training sessions held for the business, the number of inquiries directed into and out of the lab, and anything else that might indicate that the lab is proactively reaching out. When it comes to developing relationships outside the company, metrics might include: the number of POCs with vendors, the number of new tech vendor visits, conferences attended, conference presentations given, and the number of university outreach or recruiting visits.

By combining these four different metrics you will gain a better sense of your lab's progress. The critical point is agreeing on them in advance with the lab team so that everyone knows what criteria will be used to determine success. This may sound self-evident, but in the rush to get new labs started, this vital step may be omitted. Combining these criteria as part of a pre-defined and regularly applied health check creates a structure for sustainable and repeatable innovation. This in turn affords the lab insight into its big-picture value within the organization, and gives it hard metrics that lend ratification above and beyond simple profitability.

UNDERSTANDING THE TECHNOLOGY

Whether you've got an innovation team in place or are working to get one, understanding the rudiments of the technology is important. You want to demystify their activities just as you'd want a magician to reveal his or her tricks. Understanding what's going on behind the scenes will help you keep a step ahead of your lab staff, so as to properly oversee their activities. How to do this if you don't have a technical background? The first step is to disassemble the innovative technology they're plying, after which you'll be able to walk through how the components work. Typically, the fundamental elements are much the same within most tech products; what differentiates them is how they are packaged or wrapped, just as with commercial goods generally.

There are four pillar technologies that gird most of the tech your innovation lab will build or buy. These are: Social, Analytics, Cognitive or Artificial Intelligence (AI), and Blockchain. They are present to varying extents in the digital products we consume online, in the apps on our phones, or in headline-grabbing tech innovation. They are the building blocks your lab will manipulate to build new products. Understanding (in a basic way) what these technologies do is critical to understanding how your lab will exploit them.

That there are only four technologies at play doesn't mean that building digital products is easy. Quite the opposite, in fact, because tech innovators are all starting with the same toolbox. This makes it extremely difficult to develop something new. The key differential is the creativity and ingenuity of your innovation lab staffers, whose mandate is to reimagine how your clients access and consume digital products and services. They are, at best, mapping out a new digital world and unleashing forces of change that may intimidate their colleagues, who often wish that they would simply go away.

Here's a key point. Digital innovation is often less about the tech than it is about reimagining the process currently in place. A good example is a mortgage or insurance rate comparison engine, which makes purchasing these products akin to searching for and buying airline tickets. The tech is relatively straightforward, but consuming financial products in this way required the innovators to reimagine the purchase journey; the outcome is so much more efficient than shopping around that we adopt it without looking back. At the other extreme we have a product like cryptocurrencies, where path blazing technology rather than clever process engineering is the killer factor. Cryptocurrencies owe their existence to technically sophisticated and ingenious blockchain technology, which enables us to redefine and re-envision currency.

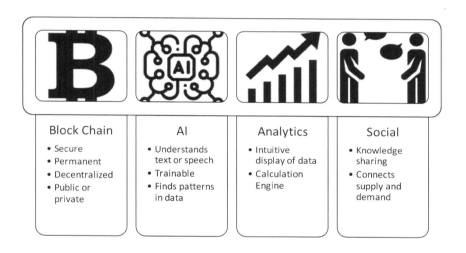

Block Chain	AI	Analytics	Social
• Secure • Permanent • Decentralized • Public or private	• Understands text or speech • Trainable • Finds patterns in data	• Intuitive display of data • Calculation Engine	• Knowledge sharing • Connects supply and demand

The four digital pillars on which most digital technology are built.

Social platforms are the nexus of many digital transformation campaigns. Digital networks allow us to encode our experiences and share them with others more easily than ever before. Sure, social media means Facebook, but equally as important are web-borne product and service ratings that show how customers perceive your company. Social is a two-way street. Now companies are engaging customers not only via customer service agents, but with artificial-intelligence driven chatbots that can interact with clients 24/7, on a multitude of platforms.

Social is everywhere, and often in an unexpected form. Some of the first fintechs in the early 2000's were peer-to-peer loan matchmakers that used social platforms to pair lenders and borrowers. These platforms were the direct descendants of Facebook, minus the messaging component. They provided a digital connectivity platform geared to the mutualization of risk, addressing a supply-and-demand problem in a completely novel way.

Car and apartment sharing sites like Uber and Airbnb are another example where social connectivity is intrinsic, yet isn't overt. Both enable a person-to-person connection by matching buyers and sellers of service. Yes, you can leave feedback, by now a familiar component of social interchange, but the heart of these businesses is connecting buyer and seller—which is equally social, even if it's not immediately evident as such. You may not see the social element in the digital products you use or buy, but if your business involves motivating a group of people to do anything, the tech likely has a social component behind the scenes that is driving the interchanges.

Of all of the technologies incorporated in digital products, analytics gets the least recognition. Probably because the calculations they perform don't capture peoples' interest, we take it for granted that any computer can do this. While this is true, analytics does a lot more than calculate. It is critical to building our digital world, since it is the means by which we visualize data. Analytics does much of the heavy lifting in the erection of digital products and services, since most of these require an efficient, accurate, and effortlessly readable data display to be effective. It also allows us to analyze the massive amount of customer data we collect throughout their journey on our websites. Analytics tells us whether our digital interactions are impactful and where they need revision.

Interestingly, AI often gets credit for a company's predictive functions—the offers of products I might want to buy, read, or listen to. In fact, these tend to be driven by simple predictive analytics. Analytics is at the core of virtually everything that's wondrous about digital. It helps convey data in an intuitively understandable way, and provides insight into future desires, based on past history. It picks our movies on Netflix, calculates the fastest route on Google Maps, picks investment portfolios in robo-advisors, shows us our health tracker progress, calculates the best insurance or mortgage deal, and when we go to sleep, monitors our credit cards for fraudulent transactions. Impressive, isn't it?

Analytics helps visualize the data we collect and gives us the dashboards that show us how our advertising or business is performing. It is the fundamental bridge between meaningless raw data and a display that helps us better understand our business world. It isn't new. We've been using Microsoft's Excel as a means of showing the meaning of numbers for decades. What is new is that today's analytic programs are making a mark in affording data visualizations minus the pain of learning Excel. Newer programs allow users to become "citizen data scientists" by allowing them to manipulate data with simple point-and-click interfaces that make analysis easy and fun. Analytics are now geared to automatically helping give the user what they want to see versus the more laborious approach of making them pick which data they want to be shown. Your lab will use lots of analytics, and they will be easy to spot at work since every chart, graph, or number evident on your interface is the product of an analytics package that is quietly going about its business.

Blockchain has two very different faces. As the technology that underlies the $100B cryptocurrency economy, its impact is massive and on the front pages of every financial publication. The explosion in initial coin offerings (ICOs) and collapsing Bitcoin and Ethereum prices are all brought to you by blockchain. There is no shortage of examples of how blockchain technology works and how it has given rise to the cryptocurrency revolution. The problem is, many people confound the specific blockchain technology used in cryptocurrency with its other iterations, applied elsewhere.

Blockchain does play a role, albeit limited, in building products available for everyday use outside of the cryptocurrency domain. Its key application is to provide a secure, public, or semi-public ledger for transactions that involve the transfer of assets, which may include payments, property deeds, contracts or anything else that depends on a trustworthy tally. Blockchain used for business applications is more correctly called "distributed ledger technology" (DLT). The ledger is "distributed" among approved users. Developers are working out the kinks in how best to use it. It is beginning to appear in loyalty points programs for everything from airlines to hamburger purchases, foreign exchange systems and anything else that needs an accurate reckoning of what is yours and mine. The technology is invisible to the end user. You'll only know you're using blockchain because invariably the platform will boast increased security and trust based on its use.

There are two problems with blockchain that hinder its adoption by most labs. First, even the "easy to deploy" version of blockchain available through large tech providers still has hundreds of configuration settings, each of which has an impact on the type of distributed network that you want to build. Understanding these configurations and their eventual impact on the network is a painstaking task. Moreover, these configurations can only be changed with difficulty once the DLT network goes live. Second, blockchain projects are wide-ranging and require that many third parties agree to use the system. This is why reward points schemes work and have been among the earliest blockchain forays. End users are incentivized with points and don't even see the underlying tech.

In contrast, with a financial transaction handled by existing systems, you would need to convince all of the parties involved that using the system will be in their best interests. This is one of the reasons why uptake of blockchain in the financial community has been slower than promised. Getting a network to agree on a system is beyond the capabilities of all but the most ambitious of labs. Add to these problems blockchain's inherently slow processing speed and high cost of computation, and you can see the obstacles that early blockchain adopters have had to overcome. This is why many who follow blockchain say that: "The first rule of blockchain is that you probably don't need blockchain." Despite these shortcomings, blockchain is a powerful tool that will undoubtedly change our future, just a bit more slowly than first predicted.

A look at our final technology is the part where the killer AIs come to take over the electronic devices near you. You most likely already use AI on your cellphone or home device with Siri, Cortana, Alexa or Google (note lack of fancy name). They already help you do simple tasks, and their cousins are probably already providing you with additional customer services at your bank or airline even if you aren't aware of it. Despite its killer reputation, AI can help your clients get answers, check balances, learn more about your company, and buy your products. It will take over many of the functions that humans provide, or at the very least route your call more efficiently to a human than the current system of pressing a number on the telephone keypad to get to the right department. Eventually, it will also do a whole lot more.

AI will take on three essential roles in digital transformation. First and perhaps most revolutionary, it will assist in the customer service side of the business. Like the science fiction movies we've been watching for years, it will support humans in providing service to your customers, giving them their first direct contact, speaking or texting, with a computer. This is a long time coming. Banks, consumer product firms, and even luxury goods companies have all installed chatbots as their first trial of this new technology. It is fascinating to see how they have been put to use. Facebook Messenger is full of these 24/7 assistants. Online brokers now have twitter-enabled chatbots that allow you to do research, check balances, and buy stock. The applications are endless. While some of the initial uses may seem frivolous, more advanced versions are coming that will provide relief from countless mouse clicks.

AI's second essential role will be enabling you to predict outcomes using your existing data. This means that you'll be able to profile customers just like Facebook, Google and Amazon do now. They know a lot about you and process that information to predict what you might want to buy or do next, right down to how often you wash your clothes and purchase laundry detergent. In short, AI will use data to spot patterns and calculate your likely desires. The same type of tech that hones your search on Google may also go to work the next time you log on to internet banking. It is spotting patterns and profiling your needs, as well as protecting you from credit card fraud, or preventing attempts at money-laundering at many large banks.

AI's third role is as the grim reaper to back-office processing in many companies. Robotic process automation is one of the most popular AI-based implementations and is being rolled out by companies everywhere. Every manager I've spoken with seems to long for the cost savings and personnel reductions that will soon be possible with a robotic staff. Using AI to process and understand documents brings it within striking distance of many jobs done by back-office workers. AI processes documents faster, cheaper, and more accurately than humans. But don't count humans out just yet. While AI is tireless, it does make mistakes. Assuming that this technology will simply eradicate your back office is a mistake especially in the early days of its implementation. Humans will have to train the AI, and clean up the inevitable errors. In the end, many customer-focused businesses will still rely on humans as the final point of contact with the customer, assisted by data and AI-generated insights. Paper-heavy back offices, like those found in so many insurers, are ripe for true disruption with AI and you will undoubtedly notice this next time you submit a claim. What will be interesting is to see how much of your interaction is with an AI or digital system and how much is human. The ease with which you can get human assistance may be at the crux of client perceptions for a good experience or bad.

These four technologies make up the pillars on which digital innovation is built. You can mix and match them to build most of the common digital products you see. Do you want a robo-advisor that helps customers select their investment portfolio? Take lots of analytics and throw in an AI chatbot to help answer questions. Want to offer cheap foreign exchange transactions? Take equal measures of analytics and social platforms and you're off to a good start— as with the fintech unicorn Transferwise. How about a password reset? Chat with a bot that runs AI voiceprint recognition, or has access to your phone's thumbprint reader, and you'll be reset in a heartbeat. Admittedly this summary doesn't cover the complex regulatory and technical hurdles that new digital products must overcome, but it serves to demonstrate how these four technologies can be aggregated to build something new.

The ability to deconstruct innovative technology into its constituent elements is critical for good innovation lab management. It's not enough to know that your lab is building innovative products; you want to have a decent grasp of how they're doing it.

Here's an example of two very different approaches. Both companies sell foreign exchange transactions, and are trying to reduce the cost of currency exchange to their clients. For the end user, the experience is almost identical: enter the amount of money to exchange, select the currency, and enter the recipient details. At this level there's no difference. Under the hood it's a different story. If this transaction is undertaken with "Transferwise," the trade is executed via a system that pairs a social network (that finds matching transactions), and an analytic engine (that performs the calculations). Its competitor, Banco Santander's One Pay FX, gives a similar result but using a DLT blockchain network run by the bank, this also teamed with an analytics engine. The results for the user are identical, but the means of attaining them couldn't be more different.

Terminology commonly used in innovation labs can be mysterious to newcomers. There are a few words and acronyms you will hear frequently. The first of these is API, which stands for application programming interface. APIs are a means of transferring information from your computer to another. Think of them as a secure gateway that allows an outside application to access data on your system. You use APIs every day when your mobile app or website accesses Google's computers to fetch a map or a search result. The API is the gateway, locked and available for only select users with passwords and authentication, or unlocked and open to all, that allows your request to be processed and information to be transmitted.

This particular technology is critical to modern digital transactions because through your own API, information that was once locked on your company servers or mainframe is now accessible to your clients. People check their bank balance, open a mobile banking app, and apply for credit cards through the API backed by the requisite security protocols. Now for the magical part. Open APIs allow others to build apps that can access your data. So for example, an app that helps users save money can access bank balances and show how much is being saved provided that the right passwords are used. Or a store's website can access Google map APIs to show a map view of where the store is located. Open APIs allow other services to feed off your data, which means that others are actively promoting your business. You might be wondering why APIs are not included as one of the four foundation technologies. APIs are really protocols or practices for accessing data rather than a technology pillar. They represent a tool for the extraction of data from your computing platform rather than a technology that your tech is "built upon." The key point is their importance to your lab and how they will help shape your future.

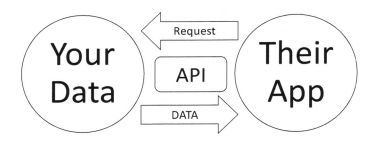

APIs are a gateway to your data allowing it to be freely accessible through apps or other services, even those developed by third parties.

Another critical term that will be frequently used in your lab is user experience (UX) design. This refers to the experience someone has when using both digital and physical services. It's an important component of customer-centricity; its intent is to make customers happy and strengthen their attachment to your brand. Given this, in certain cases the UX may be more important than the underlying tech. It is the "secret sauce" that makes the technical pieces accessible. While not one of the four pillars, it is equally important. A quick example: I have two local bank accounts and use one far more than the other, based on the ease of paying my bills and transferring funds. The underlying tech between the two banks is the same, but the superior design at one cinches why it gets my business over the other.

The final piece of tech you'll hear discussed is the internet of things (IoT), at work for all of us now. Our mobile phones produce a massive amount of data that tells where we are, how we got there and what we're doing. IoT-enabled devices are able to transfer data over a network absent a computer or human intervention. These devices may be as simple as lightbulbs and laundry machines, or as complicated as the sensors inside a gas-fired electric turbine. The key to IoT technology is that every connected device produces data that needs to be analyzed. IoT data is fed back into analytics and AI programs that show whether the data is normal, and go on to predict patterns based on usage. IoT is a data source for the four primary technologies above. In aggregate, IoT devices in your household, car, and office will transcribe even more about your activities than your cell phone does.

You should now have a better grasp of the four critical technologies and three of the tools that will be the mainstays of your lab's efforts. My intent is to give you a framework to understand what the lab will work with to achieve innovation at your company. Much of what comes out of the digital world may seem miraculous, but just a quick introduction to the fundamental tools and tech helps pull the curtain back so that the wizardry is laid bare.

CROSSING THE RUBICON WITH AI

O f the four digital pillar technologies discussed in the preceding chapter, AI is without question the tech that virtually every innovation lab out there is obsessing over. More than likely, their focus is not just on what it can do, but how to implement a successful AI project given limited AI skills within their laboratory. This isn't a unique problem. AI has come to us so quickly as a technology that most organizations, including the large tech purveyors, can't find enough AI-ready graduates. Another problem is that many labs are just now discovering what AI can really do.

AI implementation faces a quandary. We all know it can "change everything" but often we don't know exactly what, in a specific organization or domain. Even if we have an inkling, managers are challenged to find people to actually do the work. Managers and labs attempting to understand what AI can do for them are handicapped by what I call a "crisis of imagination." Most do not comprehend exactly what AI does and can do, which inevitably leads to a deep fear of getting burnt.

When discussing AI, stakeholders, including labs, tend to fall into two diametrically opposite camps. In the first are those who boldly believe that AI can solve every problem and has deity-like intelligence (or at least the intelligence of the computers on Star Trek). They not only want to do something but they want it to be big, and I mean really grandiose, because after all, it's AI. In the other camp are those—especially business unit heads!—who want nothing to do with AI, arguing that their expertise is a form of artistry that is totally incompatible with AI's limited capabilities. The first camp lives on the precipice of disappointment, while the second lives in a state of denial. Either way the results are often the same: nothing gets done.

Rather than roll out the typical pitch about how labs need to educate themselves on AI's capabilities (which I do regularly at conferences, to good effect), I thought it would be more effective to attack the other side of the problem, the fear of getting burnt. In doing so I will enter the hesitant user's psyche to question some prejudices that are stifling their creativity potential vis-a-vis AI. Are you or your lab in this group? Perhaps if I can get you to think about what you are hoping to build, and how AI might help, I can stoke the fires of imagination.

So let's dive in:

- **Start small.** Chances are the reason you have a "crisis of imagination" with AI is that you simply have never seen it at work and don't know what it can do. This goes for quite a few of your lab employees as well. Most have only passing knowledge of how it works. The fact is, you won't solve your biggest business problem with your first project. Instead think about partitioning the problem and employ a solution (or solutions) that are relevant yet simple. After you've explored AI's potential on the small scale, you'll be better situated to tackle something more significant, and more confident about utilizing the multiple technologies that large AI projects tend to require. This is why you see chatbot projects everywhere. They're one of the simplest forms of AI to work with and the starting point for many on their AI journey. They are relatively easy to build, solve real problems, and don't terrify the IT department.

- **Keep it cheap.** Don't lavish money on either your Big Four consultancy or computer company to build your first project. Now that I've offended both former colleagues and future employers, it's important to explain why I'm so blunt: I see the difficulty that both are having attracting talent. Remember, neither your IT salesperson nor the senior consulting partner will be actually doing the work. The best talent in AI is young, and is drawn to working for start-ups. If you want the best brains on the street, go there. By working with start-ups you'll be saving a fortune, get the best talent, and may develop a relationship that only improves with time. For many of those outside of your lab, this model of doing business may be fraught with the unfamiliar, especially when two 27-year-olds in ripped jeans show up in your office. Get over it, and overcome your inhibitions. This experience will benefit you on so many levels that you would be foolish not to try.

- **Look hard at open-source software.** There's so much activity in this space that brand-name AI programs may not be necessary. An open-source AI program can deliver stunning results and save you a fortune. It may also overcome thorny data privacy issues that arise when sending data to third parties if it can be hosted on your own networks. This is where the young AI companies are making their mark. They're quick to adopt free or low-cost tech, are agnostic about where to run it, and can customize better, faster, and cheaper. If you want to go for one of the big brands, and there are lots of reasons for doing this, first figure out your preferred platform. There's no use fixating on AWS if the feature set you need is better represented on MS Azure or IBM Cloud. Most of the basic AI functionality on the major purveyors' platforms are roughly comparable, so don't be obsessed on where you build so much as that you build.

- **Get your lab involved early.** Reconnoiter the playing field and you'll find that they will be both supportive and engaged in helping you. They'll be delighted you reached out, even if they can't provide much material support, because they are not experts themselves. They're in a better place to find out how to access the people and systems that will make the project successful. Somewhere in their KPIs they've already got "develop AI" as a box to be ticked off. AI is a strategic imperative for all businesses and your lab team is purpose-built for this type of work even if it's new to them.

- **Rehearse with your employees as the client.** Some managers I've talked to seem frozen in fear of letting AI loose on their actual clients. So don't. Let any initial glitches happen within the confines of your office. Build and test on your team. For example, give them a news dashboard showing sentiment analysis on your company, or AI-generated team personality profiles, or a facial recognition camera next to the coffee machine. Initially, this tech will seem like a curiosity, maybe even frivolous, but here's the payout: your lab team accrues hard skills, and your employees get face time with the technology, which will doubtless encourage thinking on how AI can make them more productive or more engaged in their work.

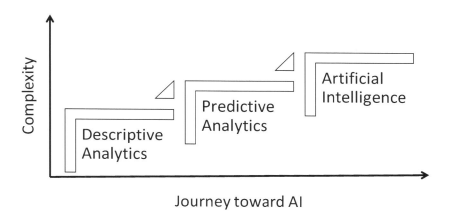

AI is part of a process that starts with basic analytics. It is not a "magic bullet" and is part of a journey that is fueled by ready access to data.

- **Get your ducks in a row in terms of analytics.** If you're interested in using AI on a set of structured data (numbers that look like they can go into Excel) you'll have to get your data in shape before you can set an AI loose. If you've got some analytics capability already built up, you're probably good to go, but if you're having difficulty accessing your data, you're better off postponing hiring the aforementioned 27-year-olds. Square away your data first, then turn on automated machine learning platforms available from major vendors.

- **Apprentice AI to your work needs.** It's not about AI doing your job, it's about you employing AI to help you do more. Even if your work is artisanal, AI can assist you with something, perhaps by bringing perspective on your market and the job you're doing within it. A great example of an artisanal workshop in most companies is the legal team. I get that they are probably the last on the list willing work with AI and your lab team. Still, how much would they benefit from the LexisNexis AI-driven sentiment analysis tools now available as a service on their most used research platform? This is not a matter of convincing anyone that AI will take over their work flow (we should be so lucky), but rather it provides them new perspectives on what it is they're doing, and more importantly, *could* be doing.

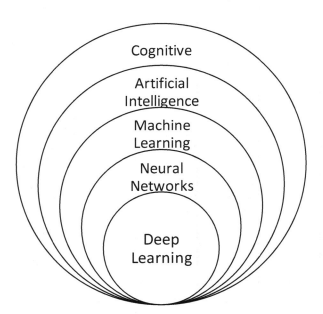

Take all self-aggrandizing tech jargon with a grain of salt. Cognitive can be used as a simple catch-all term in AI.

- **You'll hear a lot of hype about AI based on "neural nets,"** whose layers of deep learning can be both impressive and intimidating. Hopefully not from your lab staff. Take all self-aggrandizing tech jargon with a grain of salt. In the end, the AI either sees a dog when looking at a picture of a terrier or it doesn't. How it works is irrelevant. Do not be sucked into discussions about how deep "deep learning" can go, instead simply say "Show me a demo where I can see it at work." AI is fraught with big-deal labels. If you're talking about AI, Cognitive, Machine Learning, Deep Learning or Neural Networks in the most general sense, you're actually talking about the same thing (unless of course you happen to find yourself at an AI convention). Using the generic term "cognitive," as promoted by IBM, is not a bad idea because it intentionally cuts through the jargon.

- **Having AI is like having a pet.** Focus on usability, trainability and long-term maintenance costs, because anything you build will require ongoing attention. Here's the part that many who profit from the business don't like to talk about. Your AI is a never-ending project: it never stops wanting to learn new tricks and has to be trained for every one of them. This is where basic trainability and the cost of maintenance become important. Your lab team will be all over this because much of the long-term support will fall to them. Imagine running a chatbot for FAQs and having to call your AI provider for every new question or modification to existing questions. It gets annoying, even if you have a monthly maintenance program. Your users or lab team need to be able to make changes and adjustments easily.

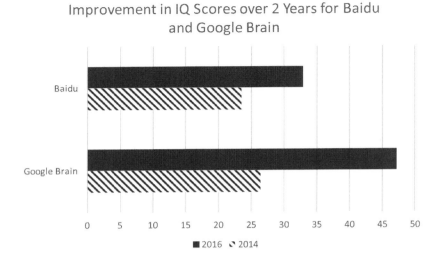

Improvement in IQ Scores over 2 Years for Baidu and Google Brain

You aren't making a lifetime commitment to your AI.
Figure that the next "new and improved" model will come around in about 18 months. Google Brain got 78% smarter in 2 years.
Source: Intelligence Quotient and Intelligence Grade of Artificial Intelligence, Annals of Data Science, June 2017, Volume 4, Issue 2, pp 179-191

- Even if your AI requires maintenance and upkeep, you're not married to it. The lifecycle of many AI projects is around 18 months before the next bigger, better, and faster model comes in and dazzles you with new capabilities. You don't necessarily need to throw away what you've built, but be prepared to work with your lab team and look hard at whether you want to upgrade or move on to a new AI system that might be purpose-built for your needs, or contain updated technology that simply makes it easier or better. The fast pace of change is fundamentally good, but is punishing for late adapters who've never built and run their first system.
- **Want to bring AI into your company but don't want to build?** Buying an AI that is configured and ready to go is one way for your lab to score points quickly. There are AI programs out there that do all sorts of things that you never

knew you needed. One of my favorites is Crystal Knows because it provides email integration and gives personality and sentiment analysis based on emails and LinkedIn profiles. If you're in a client-facing business it's a must. In finance? Go for a subscription to LikeFolio that uses sentiment analysis to make equity market predictions. Consumer product fans should check out Talk Walker to learn how AI is used to see what your customers are saying about you. Preconfigured AI tools are hitting the market daily. There are lots of people like you who want AI but don't wish to or cannot afford to build it themselves. There's no shame in buying an off-the-rack suit—if it fits like it was tailor-made.

Changing the way you and your lab think about implementing AI is the first step toward running with it in the future. Sure, there is no substitute for learning about AI through courses, demos, and sitting down with the vendors. That said, getting burned with a big investment of money, mental energy, or team resources isn't necessary to this first step. With a very modest investment your lab can build AIs that will change how you and your colleagues think about this tech.

IN SICKNESS AND IN HEALTH

Flush times make it easy to support an innovation lab. The expense is seen as a necessary business outlay and an investment in the future. But what about during bad times? What is the role of an innovation lab in your company when markets are falling and your existing business units aren't producing the returns you'd hoped for?

Bad times are unquestionably the most important time to turn to your innovation lab for the kinds of low-cost, high-return digital solutions that can help your company ride out a downturn. The reason is that your dependence on digital increases with cost pressure. Astute use of digital technology will be key to cost reductions in the operational side of business and as a means of reaching and retaining customers. Your lab is perfectly positioned to help you during this period and should be viewed as an essential player on your road to recovery.

This may not be intuitive. During a downturn an innovation lab may seem like an obvious place to cut. Its benefits are hard to monetize, and it may be unclear that innovation can contribute. Let me state loud and clear that this calculus is part of yesterday's "pre-digital" playbook. The boom in companies like Uber and Airbnb during the Great Recession (2008-2010) demonstrates why. These companies paved the way to a new, shared economy that revolutionised how we view the income potential of cars and houses. Similarly, electronic shopping tripled in usage from 2004-14, overcoming the headwinds of recession. Clearly, I'm not recommending a shift in your company's prime directive into the shared economy or online shopping. The point is, digital can help traditional companies ride out bad times. This is even more important and relevant now, with highly developed digital markets, than it was five to ten years ago. Digital is increasingly part of every company's DNA. Your lab should be the dominant force in expanding your digital presence during a downturn.

"An 'AI strategy' is separate and distinct from a 'digital strategy.' "

During tough times there is always a laser-like focus on expenses, which results in downsizing. Advances in AI are just now bringing the first virtual digital assistants and advisors to the marketplace. This technology will only advance, and more importantly, will reduce shortfalls in customer assistance caused by inevitable staff cuts to your back office and service departments. While AI can never replace your downsized staff, it can make the remaining staff more efficient, and handle new tasks with decreasing amounts of human intervention. It is precisely these advances in AI that are giving rise to the call for an "AI strategy" as separate and distinct from a "digital strategy." During a downturn, your AI strategy will be a cornerstone of your expense control efforts and, perhaps sadly, AI advances will continue to blur the difference in capabilities between human and machine.

Client retention and outreach will be another focus for your laboratory. While the aforementioned AI digital assistants and advisors will be critical, there will be other means of reaching out to clients on their terms. One will be through open APIs and partnerships that allow your goods and services to appear seamlessly on a partner's digital platform. This will allow you to participate in disseminating your brand's image outside the confines of your existing digital platform. As an example, look at PayPal, which uses its open API to allow voice commands with Apple's Siri. Users can simple say "Hey Siri send Bill $50 using PayPal." PayPal gets an entire new way to use its service, Apple gets additional utility out of Siri, and Apple customers have an easier way to send money and greater incentive to buy Apple products. Everyone wins in this scenario.

There is clearly no need to wait for a recession to use APIs, but recession will bring a greater need for your lab to investigate new opportunities for partnerships, or new uses for your library of APIs. The reason is that these are low-cost solutions that bring about new uses for your systems, and capture the investment you've made in APIs. They allow you to access new customers who may never be drawn to your product without the help of a valued partner or new capability. Your lab and IT department are just now working on creating APIs to assume major functions in your systems, and with time will develop an extensive library of them. This library is critical to your company's digital success right now, but a downturn will give rise to uses that are harder to imagine during good times.

Innovation won't stop, and just as Uber and Airbnb emerged from the Great Recession as surprise tech powerhouses, no one can predict how the next downturn will play out. What we can say is that product differentiation will be key, and that brands will have to establish their unique value proposition just as Uber and Airbnb did. Each new model will be different, but without your laboratory to investigate the new technology and survey the digital landscape, your company will be at a severe disadvantage.

DIGITAL NIRVANA AND THE FUTURE OF INNOVATION LABS

Where does this all end? Not in the immediate future for sure. None of your organizations are likely to become so digitally enlightened within the next five to ten years that they can afford to push digital to a lower priority. More likely, over this period incumbents will be putting out fires across their business lines as nimble digital upstarts and dominant tech players like Amazon and Alibaba challenge their business model. As long as this is the case, most companies will be playing a game of digital catch-up and using labs to do it. Labs are no passing fad. In fact, I would go as far as to call them the "new normal."

The trajectory of lab growth will not be entirely vertical. More likely, it will plateau as organizations better understand how much innovation they can digest and the ideal staffing levels they need to support it. Three dominant themes give rise to the need for labs: the shortage of digital skills in the business units, the pressing need to catch up and stay current with the competition, and the potential efficiencies offered by concentrating digital talent and tasks within your organization.

The shortage of digital skills will easily be around for another decade, as it takes around seven years to push students through the university system to attain advanced degrees in digital. Compounding this problem is the trend for top students to pursue careers with the top tech companies. This furthers their technological lead against non-digital industries. This trend ensures that the game of digital catch-up will become more difficult and persistent. While there will certainly be greater numbers of digitally enabled students coming through the system in coming years, an additional lag ensues in training them to be effective in your line of business. This is clearly where the labs will shine, but it takes a few more years on the timeline before your company will have the optimized skills it needs.

"Legacy management is more dangerous than legacy systems."

One of the most important jobs your lab will do is to push digital capability deeper into the business units. Even when the migration of talent is successful, the lab's role will not abruptly end. This will be a lengthy process, and business units will have to gain digital resources one-by-one. Today's lab project leaders will become tomorrow's business leaders, embedded in the business. Even under the best of circumstances there will be only a rare few from the lab ready to make this leap annually, if that. Divide the number of your business units by this small number and you'll see that it will be a long transition. Compound this with the constraints on talent and the development of new technology and it is easy to see how this is a long-term endeavour. Further attenuating this cycle is the generation of non-digital managers who won't willingly give up their jobs to upstart managers from your lab anytime soon. There is an internet meme in the fintech community that is both apropos and fair warning: "Legacy management is more dangerous than legacy systems."

The final and possibly most intractable problem is that the gap between the large tech companies and tech wannabes is growing at an exponential rate. Let's use AI as an example. This technology is being developed predominantly by large tech companies that are pouring money into their research programs and hiring the best tech talent in the world with a "money is no object" approach. The rest of the business world is left to adopt this technology only after it has been put to work by the tech giants. In hiring terms, the best we can do is to pick off an opportune hire one at a time from one of their teams, and then invest both time and effort to match their state of development in a year or two. Thereafter, the team from which your AI guru left is already on to the next big thing.

For AI in particular, growth is predicted to be exponential for at least another decade. On the brighter side, it's clear that most companies do not need to be on the "bleeding edge" of technology to be digitally competitive. But the ability to stay abreast and beat your competitors to implementing a transformational feature to your business is critical. This is what your lab is designed to do, and why it won't be going away any time soon.

Another trend that will keep your lab in the fore is that new product development will be closely tied to digital. Every new product, including the most conservative, will have a digital facet in some aspect of its sales and marketing (whether by design or not). This factor alone will require a tremendous amount of re-evaluation of product intent, sales channels, and client journeys. Your lab will be happy to provide these fresh perspectives. The notion that this will occur naturally within the product teams, even if they have some digital proficiency, is wishful thinking. As an independent entity your lab is much better positioned to give a hard and sometimes harsh evaluation of what needs to be done.

In discussions with lab managers and senior management, they've talked candidly about how long they believe they will need laboratories. One lab manager in particular comes to mind; he worked for a large and wealthy financial services company. He was young, aggressive and rose through the ranks of his company to attain his position as lab head. He had a good foundation in the business, a lesser grasp of the tech and a fatally optimistic view of the speed of digital adoption. He was certain of the span of time it would take for digital to make its mark at his company. He boldly proclaimed that within two years, the lab should "go out of business" because sufficient digital skill will have taken root in the departments it served. I respectfully disagreed, using most of the arguments just presented. I also asked him to imagine a digitally unfriendly business manager who, rather than innovate, simply awaits the lab's scheduled demise in two years.

The belief that your lab will become extinct in the short term shows a fundamental misunderstanding of the profound changes in management and process that digital will bring. It's easy to say that digital can be understood by your senior management and business unit heads in, say, six months. This may actually be true. Mandatory focused training courses can bring an awareness of what digital is and can illustrate the changes coming. What it cannot do is bring the change itself, which will take time and require a concerted, organized effort to achieve a meaningful goal. How long, you ask? Think of this along the timeframe of a decade. Humans take a share of the blame for not wanting to change, and for slowing the rate of adoption, but it goes well beyond that. Take a look at the rate of tech evolution. It is changing at such a blinding pace that we're easily looking at another decade of profound assimilation and re-assimilation simply to keep up to speed. Thinking that you're into the lab business for the short term ignores the magnitude of upheaval and undermines your future rather than buttressing it.

This is why innovation labs aren't just the latest management fad. They are an integral part of all businesses aspiring to be part of the digital revolution. If indeed this were a fad, one might easily discover the "innovation lab guru" that promises attainment of digital nirvana if you just adopt his or her prescriptive, one-size-fits-all program. The sad news is, these gurus, if they do exist, are charlatans. There aren't any easy paths to success or transformation.

Even with the best of labs, the journey to digital transformation is fraught with difficulty. The profound changes that digital brings will impact every corner of your company and no one, especially senior management, will be excluded from potential disruption. Rather than seek a guru, use your innovation lab as sherpas, and view digital transformation as your mountain to climb. You have to make the climb yourself, but the right guides can provide knowledge of the digital terrain, find the best route, do most of the heavy lifting, and provide the companionship essential for a successful summit.

BIBLIOGRAPHY

Aase, G., Roth, E., & Swaminathan, S. (2018, April).
Taking the measure of innovation. *McKinsey Quarterly*.
Retrieved from https://www.mckinsey.com/business-
functions/strategy-and-corporate-finance/our-insights/
taking-the-measure-of-innovation

Bain Insights: Two-Speed IT: Why It Ultimately Fails.
(2016, November 03). *Forbes*. Retrieved from https://
www.forbes.com/sites/baininsights/2016/11/03/
two-speed-it-why-it-ultimately-fails/#4cfe5cb3663f

Bellis, R. (2015, December 07). Why Hackathons
Are Bad for Innovation. *Fast Company*. Retrieved
from https://www.fastcompany.com/3054023/
why-hackathons-are-bad-for-innovation

Belsky, S. (2012). *Making Ideas Happen: Overcoming the Obstacles
Between Vision and Reality*. New York: Portfolio/Penguin.

Bilefield, J. (2016, April). Digital transformation: The three
steps to success. *McKinsey Quarterly*. Retrieved from https://
www.mckinsey.com/business-functions/digital-mckinsey/
our-insights/digital-transformation-the-three-steps-to-success.

Blank, S. (2015, December 8). How to Avoid Innovation
Theater: The Six Decisions to Make Before Establishing
an Innovation Outpost. Retrieved from https://steveblank.
com/2015/12/08/the-six-critical-decisions-to-make-before-
establishing-an-innovation-outpost/

Blank, S. (2015, December 17). How to Set Up a
Corporate Innovation Outpost That Works. Retrieved
from https://steveblank.com/2015/12/17/
how-to-set-up-a-corporate-innovation-outpost/

Bossert, O., Ip, C., & Laartz, J. (2014, December). A two-speed IT architecture for the digital enterprise. *McKinsey Quarterly*. Retrieved from https://www.mckinsey.com/business-functions/digital-mckinsey/our-insights/a-two-speed-it-architecture-for-the-digital-enterprise

Broussard, M. (2015, July 08). The Secret Lives of Hackathon Junkies. *The Atlantic*. Retrieved from https://www.theatlantic.com/technology/archive/2015/07/the-secret-lives-of-hackathon-junkies/397895/

Brown, D. (2018, April 23). People, Not Technology, Are Key to Digital Transformation. *Forbes*. Retrieved from https://www.forbes.com/sites/forbestechcouncil/2018/04/23/people-not-technology-are-key-to-digital-transformation/#19259a4b3cac

Bry, N. (2018, May 30). Innovation Labs: Open innovation, outside and inside the corporation (4/4). Retrieved from https://nbry.wordpress.com/2018/05/30/innovation-labs-open-innovation-outside-and-inside-the-corporation-4-4/

CB Insights (2018, January 11). JPMorgan Chase Competitive Strategy Teardown: How the Bank Stacks Up on Fintech & Innovation. Retrieved from https://www.cbinsights.com/research/jpmorgan-chase-competitive-strategy-teardown-expert-intelligence/

Chan, K. (2017, November 13). Experimenting in innovation labs. *The Business Times*. Retrieved from https://www.businesstimes.com.sg/hub-projects/singapore-fintech-festival-2017/experimenting-in-innovation-labs

Chishti, S., & Barberis, J. (2016). *The FINTECH Book: The Financial Technology Handbook for Investors, Entrepreneurs and Visionaries*. Chichester: Wiley.

Chishti, S., & Puschmann, T. (2018). *The WEALTHTECH Book: The FinTech Handbook for Investors, Entrepreneurs and Finance Visionaries*. Chichester, West Sussex, United Kingdom: Wiley.

Christensen, C. (2011). *The Innovator's Dilemma: The Revolutionary Book That Will Change the Way You Do Business*. New York, NY: Harper Business.

Christensen, C., Kaufman, S., Shih, W. (2019, January 08). Innovation Killers: How Financial Tools Destroy Your Capacity to Do New Things. *Harvard Business Review*.

DBS Asia X: Fresh innovation at a galaxy not so far away. (n.d.). Retrieved from https://www.dbs.com/innovation/dbs-innovates/spaces-dax.html

Demchuk, S. (2018, November 28). Why Banks Must Ditch the 'Build vs. Buy' Mentality and Embrace a Platform Approach. Retrieved from https://devops.com/why-banks-must-ditch-the-build-vs-buy-mentality-and-embrace-a-platform-approach/

Dyer, J., Gregersen, H., & Christensen, C. (2011). *The Innovator's DNA: Mastering the Five Skills of Disruptive Innovators*. Boston: Harvard Business Review Press.

Expedia transforms travel through technology. (2017, May 02). Retrieved from https://www.digitalnewsasia.com/business/expedia-transforms-travel-through-technology

Gryszkiewicz, L., Toivonen, T., & Lykourentzou, I. (2016, November 3). Innovation Labs: 10 Defining Features. *Stanford Social Innovation Review*. Retrieved from https://ssir.org/articles/entry/innovation_labs_10_defining_features

Heath, C., & Heath, D. (2008). *Made to Stick: Why Some Ideas Survive and Others Die*. New York: Random House.

How Do You Measure Innovation Results and Outcomes? *Innovation Management*. (n.d.). Retrieved from http://www.innovationmanagement.se/imtool-articles/how-do-you-measure-innovation-results-and-outcomes/

Kim, W. C., & Mauborgne, R. (2015). *Blue Ocean Strategy, Expanded Edition: How to Create Uncontested Market Space and Make the Competition Irrelevant*. Boston, MA: Harvard Business Review Press.

King, B. (2013). *Bank 3.0: Why Banking Is No Longer Somewhere You Go, But Something You Do.* Singapore: Marshall Cavendish Editions.

King, B. (2014). *Breaking Banks: The Innovators, Rogues, and Strategists Rebooting Banking.* Singapore: Wiley.

King, B. (2018). *Bank 4.0: Banking Everywhere, Never at a Bank.* Singapore: Marshall Cavendish Business.

Kirsner, S. (2015, May 06). What Big Companies Get Wrong About Innovation Metrics. *Harvard Business Review.* Retrieved from https://hbr.org/2015/05/what-big-companies-get-wrong-about-innovation-metrics

Laloux, F. (2014). *Reinventing Organizations: A Guide to Creating Organizations Inspired by the Next Stage of Human Consciousness.* Brussels, Belgium: Nelson Parker.

Lee, K. (2018). *AI Superpowers: China, Silicon Valley, and the New World Order.* Boston: Houghton Mifflin Harcourt.

Liu, F., Shi, Y., & Liu, Y. (2017). Intelligence Quotient and Intelligence Grade of Artificial Intelligence. *Annals of Data Science, 4*(2), 179-191. doi:10.1007/s40745-017-0109-0

Lumen Lab (n.d.). *What We Do.* Retrieved from http://lumenlab.sg/what-we-do/

Macheel, T. (2017, September 14). Avoid 'FOMO': Why banks need to focus on humans, not tech. Retrieved from https://tearsheet.co/culture-and-talent/avoid-fomo-why-banks-need-to-focus-on-humans-not-tech/

Manulife (2016, September 29). *LOFT: Lab of Forward Thinking News and Events.* Retrieved from http://manulife.force.com/Master-Article-Detail?content_id=a0Q5000000KHqxlEAD&ocmsLang=en_US

Maurya, A. (2017). *Running Lean: Iterate from Plan A to a Plan That Works.* Sebastopol, CA: O'Reilly.

McConnell, P. (2017). *Strategic Technology Risk.* London: Risk Books.

McConnell, P. (2017, September 12). Why no one can handle technology risk. Retrieved from https://

www.risk.net/risk-management/5328591/
why-no-one-can-handle-technology-risk

Robinson, A. (2017, October 12). 4 Things You Must Consider Before Building Software. Retrieved from https://www.inc. com/adam-robinson/4-things-you-must-consider-before-building-software.html

Sironi, P. & Ravezzi, M. (2017). *MiFID II: Value-Generation for Investors*. Place of publication not identified: Risk Books.

Sironi, P. (2016). *FinTech Innovation: From Robo-Advisors to Goal Based Investing and Gamification*. Chichester, West Sussex: Wiley.

Skinner, C. (2014). *Digital Bank: Strategies to Launch or Become a Digital Bank*. Asia: Marshall Cavendish International

Skinner, C. (2018). *Digital Human: The Fourth Revolution of Humanity Includes Everyone*. Asia: Marshall Cavendish International

Solaria Labs: An Innovation Incubator. (n.d.). Retrieved from https://www.solarialabs.com/

Solodkiy, V. (2017). *The First Fintech Bank's Arrival*. Singapore: Amazon Digital Services.

Space10. (2018, November 22). Highlights from Three Years of SPACE10. Retrieved from https://space10.io/ highlights-from-three-years-of-space10/

Taleb, N. (2010). *The Black Swan: The Impact of the Highly Improbable*. New York: Random House Trade Paperbacks.

Taleb, N. (2016). *Antifragile: Things That Gain from Disorder*. New York: Random House.

Taleb, N. (2018). *Skin in the Game: Hidden Asymmetries in Daily Life*. New York: Random House.

Top 28 Fintech and Insurtech Innovation Labs in Singapore. (2018, November 16). Retrieved from http://fintechnews.sg/26093/fintech/ top-28-fintech-and-insurtech-innovation-labs-in-singapore/

Tucker, R. (2017, November 20). Starting an Innovation Lab? Avoid These Pitfalls. *Forbes*. Retrieved from https://www. forbes.com/sites/robertbtucker/2017/11/20/starting-an-innovation-lab-avoid-these-pitfalls/#4dda57c27a2b

VanderLinden, S., Millie, S., Anderson, S., & Chishti, S. (2018). *The INSURTECH Book*: *The Insurance Technology Handbook for Investors, Entrepreneurs and FinTech Visionaries*. Chichester, West Sussex, United Kingdom: Wiley.

Viki, T. (2018, August 12). Why Does Your Innovation Lab Exist? *Forbes*. Retrieved from https://www.forbes.com/sites/tendayiviki/2018/08/12/why-does-your-innovation-lab-exist/#7e95cb671e45

Viki, T. (2018, April 15). The Myth of the Innovation Lab. *Forbes*. Retrieved from https://www.forbes.com/sites/tendayiviki/2018/04/15/the-myth-of-the-innovation-lab/#10285aa64125

Viki, T. (2018, September 23). The Three Human Barriers to Digital Transformation. *Forbes*. Retrieved from https://www.forbes.com/sites/tendayiviki/2018/09/23/the-three-human-barriers-to-digital-transformation/#300c63ef164b

X, The Moonshot Factory. (n.d.). Retrieved from https://x.company/

ABOUT THE AUTHOR

Richard Turrin is an award-winning executive with more than 20 years of experience in fintech innovation. He is now an independent fintech and AI consultant, helping clients navigate the uncharted waters associated with the latest cognitive technologies.

Rich headed fintech for **IBM** Cognitive Studios Singapore (IBM's Innovation Lab) where he led a team that built innovative AI and analytic solutions. He also worked in **IBM** China where he led his team to win the prestigious "Risk Technology Product of the Year" award for his unique hybrid-cloud solution to risk analytics.

Rich was a banker for almost 20 years and a serial innovator throughout his career. Specializing in the design and innovation of new fixed-income products, he saw firsthand how technology, finance, and regulation come together to impact innovation. He made his career by thinking "out of the box" and uses this experience to put fintech and AI to work for his clients.

He is a co-author in the recently launched "InsurTech" book, and enjoys spreading the message of digital transformation through conferences and blog posts. Most of all, he enjoys building teams and systems that solve real problems.

As a consultant he focuses on people, not just tech, since in his experience people's relation to tech is the key to innovation. Learn more: RichTurrin.com.

HELP ME BY BEING INNOVATIVE AND EXCELLENT

If you enjoyed reading *Innovation Lab Excellence,* would you mind taking a minute to write a review on Amazon? Even a short review helps and it would mean a lot to me.

If someone you know is working in or around an innovation laboratory please send them a copy of this book. Whether you gift it to them through Amazon or send them to richturrin.com to get the opening chapters free, please help spread the word.

If you would like to bulk order copies of this book for your company or innovation lab team please reach out to me on richturrin.com.

Finally, if you'd like to get free bonus materials from this book, be part of the innovation lab discussion, and receive updates on my writings, you can sign up on richturrin.com and connect on LinkedIn: linkedin.com/in/turrin.

Go innovate!

Made in the USA
Coppell, TX
16 July 2023